LANGENSCHEIDT - LEKTÜRE 66
A STEINBECK READER

Langenscheidt-Lektüre 66

# A Steinbeck Reader

Vier Kurzgeschichten des großen
amerikanischen Erzählers
und Nobelpreisträgers John Steinbeck

LANGENSCHEIDT
BERLIN · MÜNCHEN · WIEN · ZÜRICH

Wir danken Elaine A. Steinbeck für die Erlaubnis,
die vier Kurzgeschichten in dieser Lektürereihe zu veröffentlichen.

| Auflage: | 11. | 10. | 9. | 8. | 7. | Letzte Zahlen |
|---|---|---|---|---|---|---|
| Jahr: | 1995 | 94 | 93 | 92 | 91 | maßgeblich |

FLIGHT: *Copyright © 1938 by John Steinbeck.*
*Copyright renewed.*
THE HARNESS: *Copyright © 1938 by John Steinbeck.*
*Copyright renewed.*
THE MURDER: *Copyright © 1934 by John Steinbeck.*
*Copyright renewed.*
THE VIGILANTE: *Copyright © 1936 by John Steinbeck.*
*Copyright renewed.*

*© 1974 Langenscheidt KG, Berlin und München*
*Druck: Druckhaus Langenscheidt, Berlin-Schöneberg*
*Printed in Germany · ISBN 3-468-44660-8*

# Vorwort

Seit John Steinbeck (1902–1968) mit einem Schelmenroman über die armen mexikanischen Bauern („Tortilla Flat", 1935) hervortrat, gehört er zu den bekanntesten und beliebtesten Schriftstellern unserer Zeit. Sein Einsatz für die Besitzlosen und die von Natur und Gesellschaft vernachlässigten Menschen brachte ihm besonders mit seinen frühen Werken „Of Mice and Men", „Grapes of Wrath" weltweiten Ruhm. In Deutschland ist Steinbeck auch durch die Verfilmung seines Romans „East of Eden" („Jenseits von Eden") einem breiten Publikum zum Begriff geworden. Die meisten seiner Romane und Kurzgeschichten liegen in deutscher Übersetzung vor. 1940 erhielt Steinbeck den Pulitzer-Preis für „Grapes of Wrath" und 1962 den Nobelpreis für Literatur.

Die vier Kurzgeschichten dieses Lektürebandes sind der bekannten short-story-Sammlung „The Long Valley" entnommen. Wenn Steinbeck vor dem Hintergrund einer großartigen kalifornischen Landschaft von seinen urwüchsig primitiven, in ihrer Einfalt rührenden Menschen erzählt, so werden sie durch seine Erzählkunst mit prallem Leben erfüllt: Der Leser weiß, wie sie aussehen, wie sie denken, wie sie handeln und was sie fühlen. Er nimmt aber auch teil an der kritischen Einstellung Steinbecks gegenüber seiner Umgebung und seinen Mitmenschen. Bei der Darstellung eines sinnlosen Lynchmordes in der letzten Erzählung des vorliegenden Bandes, in „The Vigilante", findet Steinbeck feinere, leisere Töne, um seiner Kritik mit sprachlichen Mitteln, sozusagen zwischen den Zeilen, Ausdruck zu verleihen.

Die Lektüre der Kurzgeschichten wird erleichtert durch die Angabe der Übersetzung und Aussprache der weniger bekannten Vokabeln in einer Vokabelspalte. Wörter, die in der Vokabelspalte enthalten sind, werden im laufenden Text mit einem kleinen Kreis gekennzeichnet. Der Leser erspart sich dadurch vergebliches Suchen. Er kommt schneller voran.

LANGENSCHEIDT

# Inhaltsverzeichnis

# Erklärung der Aussprachebezeichnung

## A. Vokale und Diphthonge

[ɑ:] reines langes a, wie in Vater, kam, Schwan: *far* [fɑ:], *father* ['fɑ:ðə].

[ʌ] kommt im Deutschen nicht vor. Kurzes dunkles a, bei dem die Lippen nicht gerundet sind. Vorn und offen gebildet: *butter* ['bʌtə], *come* [kʌm], *colour* ['kʌlə], *blood* [blʌd], *flourish* ['flʌriʃ], *twopence* ['tʌpəns].

[æ] heller, ziemlich offener, nicht zu kurzer Laut. Raum zwischen Zunge und Gaumen noch größer als bei ä in Ähre: *fat* [fæt], *man* [mæn].

[ɛə] nicht zu offenes halblanges ä; im Englischen nur vor r, das als ein dem ä nachhallendes ə erscheint: *bare* [bɛə], *pair* [pɛə], *there* [ðɛə].

[ai] Bestandteile: helles, zwischen ɑ: und æ liegendes a und schwächeres offenes i. Die Zunge hebt sich halbwegs zur i-Stellung: *I* [ai], *lie* [lai], *dry* [drai].

[au] Bestandteile: helles, zwischen ɑ: und æ liegendes a und schwächeres offenes u: *house* [haus], *now* [nau].

[ei] halboffenes e, nach i auslautend, indem die Zunge sich halbwegs zur i-Stellung hebt: *date* [deit], *play* [plei], *obey* [ə'bei].

[e] halboffenes kurzes e, etwas geschlossener als das e in Bett: *bed* [bed], *less* [les].

[ə] flüchtiger Gleitlaut, ähnlich dem deutschen, flüchtig gesprochenen e in Gelage: *about* [ə'baut], *butter* ['bʌtə], *connect* [kə'nekt].

[əu] mit [ə] beginnend und in schwaches u auslautend; keine Rundung der Lippen, kein Heben der Zunge: *note* [nəut], *boat* [bəut], *below* [bi'ləu].

[i:] langes i, wie in lieb, Bibel, aber etwas offener einsetzend als im Deutschen; wird in Südengland doppellautig gesprochen, indem sich die Zunge allmählich zur i-Stellung hebt: *scene* [si:n], *sea* [si:], *feet* [fi:t], *ceiling* ['si:liŋ].

[i] kurzes offenes i wie in bin, mit: *big* [big], *city* ['siti].

[iə] halboffenes halblanges i mit nachhallendem ə: *here* [hiə], *hear* [hiə], *inferior* [in'fiəriə].

[ɔ:] offener langer, zwischen a und o schwebender Laut: *fall* [fɔ:l], *nought* [nɔ:t], *or* [ɔ:], *before* [bi'fɔ:].

[ɔ] offener kurzer, zwischen a und o schwebender Laut, offener als das o in Motte: *god* [gɔd], *not* [nɔt], *wash* [wɔʃ], *hobby* ['hɔbi].

[ɔi] Bestandteile: offenes o und schwächeres offenes i. Die Zunge hebt sich halbwegs zur i-Stellung: *voice* [vɔis], *boy* [bɔi], *annoy* [ə'nɔi].

[ə:] im Deutschen fehlender Laut; offenes langes ö, etwa wie gedehnt gesprochenes ö in öffnen, Mörder; kein Vorstülpen oder Runden der Lippen; kein Heben der Zunge: *word* [wə:d], *girl* [gə:l], *learn* [lə:n], *murmur* ['mə:mə].

[u:] langes u wie in Buch, doch ohne Lippenrundung; vielfach diphthongisch als halboffenes langes u mit nachhallendem geschlossenem u: *fool* [fu:l], *shoe* [ʃu:], *you* [ju:], *rule* [ru:l], *canoe* [kə'nu:].

[uə] halboffenes halblanges u mit nachhallendem ə: *poor* [puə], *sure* [ʃuə], *allure* [ə'ljuə].

[u] flüchtiges u: *put* [put], *look* [luk], *careful* ['kɛəful].

Ganz vereinzelt werden auch die folgenden französischen Laute gebraucht: Die Nasale [ã] wie in frz. *blanc*, [ɔ̃] wie in frz. *bonbon* und [ɛ̃] wie in frz. *vin*, sowie die drei Vokale [o] wie in frz. *chaud*, [ɛ] wie in frz. *belle* und [ø] wie in frz. *monsieur*.

Die **Länge eines Vokals** wird durch [ː] bezeichnet, z. B. *ask* [ɑːsk], *astir* [əˈstəː]. Die **Betonung** der englischen Wörter wird durch das Zeichen [ˈ] vor der zu betonenden Silbe angegeben, z. B. *onion* [ˈʌnjən].


# B. Konsonanten

[r] nur vor Vokalen gesprochen. Völlig verschieden vom deutschen Zungenspitzen- oder Zäpfchen-r. Die Zungenspitze bildet mit der oberen Zahnwulst eine Enge, durch die der Ausatmungsstrom mit Stimmton hindurchgetrieben wird, ohne den Laut zu rollen. Am Ende eines Wortes wird r nur bei Bindung mit dem Anlautvokal des folgenden Wortes gesprochen: *rose* [rəuz], *pride* [praid], *there is* [ðɛərˈiz].

[ʒ] stimmhaftes sch, wie g in Genie, j in Journal: *azure* [ˈæʒə], *jazz* [dʒæz], *jeep* [dʒiːp], *large* [lɑːdʒ].

[ʃ] stimmloses sch, wie im Deutschen Schnee, rasch: *shake* [ʃeik], *washing* [ˈwɔʃiŋ], *lash* [læʃ].

[θ] im Deutschen nicht vorhandener stimmloser Lispellaut; durch Anlegen der Zunge an die oberen Schneidezähne hervorgebracht: *thin* [θin], *path* [pɑːθ], *method* [ˈmeθəd].

[ð] derselbe Laut stimmhaft, d. h. mit Stimmton: *there* [ðɛə], *breathe* [briːð], *father* [ˈfɑːðə].

[s] stimmloser Zischlaut, entsprechend dem deutschen ß in Spaß, reißen: *see* [siː], *hats* [hæts], *decide* [diˈsaid].

[z] stimmhafter Zischlaut wie im Deutschen sausen: *zeal* [ziːl], *rise* [raiz], *horizon* [həˈraizn].

[ŋ] wird wie der deutsche Nasenlaut in fangen, singen gebildet: *ring* [riŋ], *singer* [ˈsiŋə].

[ŋk] derselbe Laut mit nachfolgendem k wie im Deutschen senken, Wink: *ink* [iŋk], *tinker* [ˈtiŋkə].

[w] flüchtiges, mit Lippe an Lippe gesprochenes w, aus der Mundstellung für u: gebildet: *will* [wil], *swear* [swɛə], *queen* [kwiːn].

[f] stimmloser Lippenlaut wie im Deutschen flott: *fat* [fæt], *tough* [tʌf], *effort* [ˈefət].

[v] stimmhafter Lippenlaut wie im Deutschen Vase, Ventil: *vein* [vein], *velvet* [ˈvelvit].

[j] flüchtiger zwischen j und i schwebender Laut: *onion* [ˈʌnjən], *yes* [jes], *filial* [ˈfiljəl].

# Verwandte Abkürzungen

| | | | |
|---|---|---|---|
| ○ | vor einem englischen Wort im Text zeigt an, daß dieses Wort in der Vokabelspalte übersetzt wird. | *j–m* | jemandem |
| | | *j–n* | jemanden |
| | | *j–s* | jemandes |
| | | *m–e* | meine |
| | | *m–r* | meiner |
| *Abkzg* | Abkürzung | *m–s* | meines |
| AE | amerikanisches Englisch | od., *od.* | oder |
| | | *Pl* | Plural |
| BE | britisches Englisch | *s–e* | seine |
| *e–e* | eine | *s–r* | seiner |
| *e–r* | einer | *s–s* | seines |
| *e–s* | eines | *sl.* | Slang |
| *et.* | etwas | s.o. | someone |
| *etc.* | und so weiter | *Span.* | Spanisch |
| F | Familiär (= Umgangssprache) | s.th. | something |
| | | *u.* | und |

# Flight

About fifteen miles below °Monterey, on the wild coast, the Torres family had their farm, a few °sloping acres above a cliff that °dropped to the brown °reefs and to the °hissing white waters of the ocean. Behind the farm the stone mountains °stood up against the sky. The farm buildings °huddled like little °clinging °aphids on the °mountain skirts, °crouched low to the ground as though the wind might blow them into the sea. The little °shack, the rattling, °rotting °barn were °grey-bitten with sea salt, °beaten by the damp wind until they °had taken on the color of the °granite hills. Two horses, a red cow and a red calf, half a dozen pigs and a °flock of °lean, °multi-colored chickens °stocked the place. A little °corn was °raised on the °sterile °slope, and it grew short and thick °under the wind, and all the °cobs °formed on the landward sides of the °stalks.

Mama Torres, a lean, °dry woman with °ancient eyes, had °ruled the farm for ten years, °ever since her husband °tripped over a stone in the field one day and fell °full length on a °rattlesnake. When one is bitten on the chest there is not much that can be done.

Mama Torres had three children, two °undersized black ones of twelve and fourteen, Emilio and Rosy, whom Mama °kept fishing on the °rocks be-

Monterey [mɔntə'rei] *Stadt u. Halbinsel südöstl. von San Franzisko, Kalifornien.*
sloping ['sloupiŋ] *schräg, abfallend, ansteigend*
dropped [drɔpt] *von* drop [drɔp] *hier: (steil) abfallen*
reef [riːf] *Riff*
hissing ['hisiŋ] *zischend*
stood up against [stud] *von* stand up against [stænd] *sich erheben gegen*
huddle ['hʌdl] *hier: kleben*
clinging ['kliŋiŋ] *sich anklammernd*
aphid ['eifid] *Blattlaus*
mountain skirts *Pl* [skəːts] *hier: Fuß der Berge*
crouch [krautʃ] *sich ducken*
shack [ʃæk] *Hütte*
rotting ['rɔtiŋ] *verfaulend*
barn [bɑːn] *Stall; Scheune*
grey-bitten ['greibitn] *zu e-m Grau zerfressen*
beaten ['biːtn] *von* beat [biːt] *schlagen, hier: peitschen*
had taken on ['teikən] *von* take on [teik] *annehmen*
granite ['grænit] *Granit(...)*
flock [flɔk] *Schar*
lean [liːn] *mager; hager*
multi-colored AE ['mʌlti] *bunt*
stock [stɔk] *hier: bilden das lebende Inventar*
corn AE [kɔːn] *Mais*
raise [reiz] *anbauen*
sterile ['sterail] *unfruchtbar*
slope [sloup] *(Ab)Hang*
under the wind *dem Wind ausgesetzt*
cob [kɔb] *Maiskolben*
form [fɔːm] *sich bilden*
stalk [stɔːk] *Stengel*
dry [drai] *verblüht, verwelkt*
ancient ['einʃənt] *(ur)alt*
rule [ruːl] *bewirtschaften*
ever since *seit der Zeit*

13

low the farm when the sea was kind and when the °truant officer was in some distant part of Monterey °County. And there was Pepé, the tall smiling son of nineteen, a gentle, °affectionate boy, but very lazy. Pepé had a tall head, °pointed at the top, and from its °peak, °coarse black hair grew down like a °thatch all around. Over his smiling little eyes Mama cut a straight °bang so he could see. Pepé had °sharp Indian cheek bones and an °eagle nose, but his mouth was as sweet and °shapely as a girl's mouth, and his chin was °fragile and °chiseled. He was °loose and °gangling, all legs and feet and °wrists, and he was very lazy. Mama °thought him °fine and °brave, but she never told him so. She said, "Some lazy cow must have got into °thy father's family, else how could I have a son like °thee." And she said, "When I °carried thee, a °sneaking lazy °coyote came out of the °brush and looked at me one day. That must have made thee so."

Pepé smiled °sheepishly and °stabbed at the ground with his knife to °keep the °blade sharp and free from rust. °It was his inheritance, that knife, his father's knife. The long heavy blade °folded back into the black handle. There was a button on the handle. When Pepé pressed the button, the blade °leaped out °ready for use. The knife was with Pepé always, for it had been his father's knife.

One sunny morning when the sea below the cliff was °glinting and blue and the white °surf °creamed on the reef,

trip *stolpern, straucheln*
full length [leŋθ] *der Länge nach*
rattlesnake ['rætlsneik] *Klapperschlange*
undersized ['ʌndə'saizd] *winzig, hier: unterentwickelt*
kept [kept] *von* keep [ki:p] *hier: lassen, anhalten zu*
rock [rɔk] *Fels(en)*

---

truant officer ['tru:(:)ənt] *Beamter, der häufiges unentschuldigtes Fernbleiben vom Schulunterricht zu untersuchen hat*
county AE ['kaunti] *(Verwaltungs)Bezirk, Kreis*
affectionate [ə'fekʃnit] *anhänglich*
pointed ['pɔintid] *spitz (zulaufend)*
peak [pi:k] *Scheitel(punkt)*
coarse [kɔ:s] *grob, derb, hier: kräftig*
thatch [θætʃ] *Strohdach; hier: F Haarwald*
bang [bæŋ] *Pony (Frisur)*
sharp [ʃɑ:p] *hervortretend*
eagle nose ['i:gl nəuz] *Adlernase*
shapely ['ʃeipli] *wohlgeformt, hübsch*
fragile ['frædʒail] *zart*
chiseled ['tʃizld] *scharf geschnitten*
loose [lu:s] *schlaksig*
gangling ['gæŋgliŋ] *(hoch) aufgeschossen*
wrist [rist] *Handgelenk*
thought him ... [θɔ:t] *von* think s.o. to be s.th. [θiŋk] *j-n für et. halten*
fine [fain] *hier: stattlich*
brave [breiv] *mutig, tapfer*
thy [ðai] = your *dein(e)*
thee [ði:] = you *dich; dir*
carried ['kærid] *von* carry ['kæri] *(unter dem Herzen) tragen*
sneaking ['sni:kiŋ] *hinterlistig*
coyote ['kɔiəut] *Prärie-, Steppenwolf, Kojote*
brush [brʌʃ] *Strauchwerk, Gebüsch; Dickicht, Unterholz*

when even the stone mountains looked kindly, Mama Torres called °out the door of the shack, "Pepé, I have a labor for thee."

There was no answer. Mama listened. From behind the barn she heard a °burst of laughter. She lifted her °full long skirt and walked in the direction of the noise.

Pepé was sitting on the ground with his back against a box. His white teeth °glistened. °On either side of him stood the two black ones, °tense and °expectant. Fifteen feet away a °redwood °post was °set in the ground. Pepé's right hand lay °limply in his °lap, and in the °palm the big black knife rested. The blade was °closed back into the handle. Pepé looked smiling at the sky.

Suddenly Emilio cried, °"Ya!"

Pepé's wrist °flicked like the head of a snake. The blade seemed to °fly open in mid-air, and with a °thump the point °dug into the redwood post, and the black handle °quivered. The three °burst into °excited laughter. Rosy ran to the post and pulled out the knife and brought it back to Pepé. He closed the blade and °settled the knife carefully in his °listless palm again. He grinned °self-consciously at the sky.

"Ya!"

The heavy knife °lanced out and sunk into the post again. Mama moved forward like a ship and °scattered the play.

"All day you do foolish things with the knife, like a °toy-baby," she °stormed. "Get up on thy °huge feet that eat up shoes. Get up!" She took him

sheepish ['ʃiːpiʃ] einfältig, linkisch
stab at [stæb] hier: stoßen in
keep (er)halten, schützen vor
blade [bleid] Klinge
it was his inheritance [in'heritəns] er hatte es geerbt
fold back [fəuld] sich zusammenklappen lassen
leap out [liːp] herausschnellen
ready for use ['redi, juːs] gebrauchsfertig
glinting ['glintiŋ] glänzend
surf [sɔːf] Brandung
cream [kriːm] schäumen

out (of) zu ... hinaus
burst of laughter [bəːst, 'lɑːftə] Lachsalve, Gelächter
full [ful] weit
glisten ['glisn] hier: blitzen
on either side ['aiðə said] hier: links u. rechts
tense [tens] (an)gespannt
expectant [iks'pektənt] erwartungsvoll
redwood ['redwud] Rotholz (-baum), Sequoie
post [pəust] Pfosten, Pfahl
set in the ground [graund] hier: in den Boden eingelassen od. gerammt
limp [limp] schlaff
lap [læp] Schoß
palm [pɑːm] hohle Hand
closed back [kləuzd] hier: zurückgeklappt
ya! [ja] (Span.) jetzt!
flick vor-, herumschnellen
fly open in mid-air [flai, 'əupən, 'mid'eə] sich mitten im Flug öffnen
thump [θʌmp] dumpfer Schlag
dug into [dʌg] von dig into [dig] hier: sich bohren in
quiver ['kwivə] zittern, beben
burst into laughter in Gelächter ausbrechen
excited [ik'saitid] aufgeregt
settle ['setl] hier: betten, legen
listless ['listlis] schlaff, matt
self-conscious ['self'kɔnʃəs] befangen, unsicher

15

by one °loose shoulder and °hoisted at him. Pepé grinned sheepishly and came °half-heartedly to his feet. "Look!" Mama cried. "Big °lazy, you must catch the horse and put on him thy father's saddle. You must ride to Monterey. The medicine bottle is empty. There is no salt. Go °thou now, °Peanut! Catch the horse."

A °revolution °took place in the °relaxed °figure of Pepé. "To Monterey, °me? Alone? °Sí, Mama."

She °scowled at him. "Do not think, big sheep, that you will buy °candy. No, I will give you only enough for the medicine and the salt."

Pepé smiled. "Mama, °you will put the °hatband on the hat?"

She °relented then. "Yes, Pepé. You may wear the hatband."

His voice °grew °insinuating, "And the green °handkerchief, Mama?"

"Yes, if you go quickly and return with no trouble, the silk green handkerchief °will go. If you make sure to °take off the handkerchief when you eat so no spot may fall on it...."

"*Sí*, Mama. I will be careful. I am a man."

"Thou? A man? Thou °art a peanut."

He went into the °rickety barn and brought out a rope, and he walked °agilely enough up the hill to catch the horse.

When he was ready and °mounted before the door, mounted on his father's saddle that was so old that the °oaken frame showed through °torn leather in many places, then Mama brought out the round black hat with

lance out [lɑːns] *hier: die Luft durchschneiden*
scatter the play ['skætə, pleɪ] *das Spiel jäh beenden*
toy-baby ['tɔɪbeɪbɪ] *Kleinstkind*
storm [stɔːm] *toben, donnern*
huge [hjuːdʒ] *riesig, riesengroß*

---

loose *hier: schlaff*
hoist [hɔɪst] *hochziehen*
half-hearted ['hɑːfˈhɑːtɪd] *lustlos*
lazy = lazy-bones ['leɪzɪbəʊnz] *Faulpelz*
thou [ðaʊ] = you *du*
peanut ['piːnʌt] *Erdnuß; hier: AE halbe Portion, Wicht*
revolution [revəˈluːʃən] (*radikale*) *Veränderung*
took place [tʊk pleɪs] *von* take place *stattfinden, hier: vorgehen*
relaxed [rɪˈlækst] *entspannt, schlaff*
figure ['fɪgə] *Gestalt*
me F = I
sí [sɪ] (*Span.*) *ja, jawohl*
scowl at s.o. [skaʊl] *j-n finster anblicken*
candy AE ['kændɪ] *Süßigkeiten Pl*
you will = will you
hatband ['hætbænd] *Hutband*
relent [rɪˈlent] *sich erweichen lassen, weich werden*
grew [gruː] *von* grow [grəʊ] *werden*
insinuating [ɪnˈsɪnjʊeɪtɪŋ] (*ein-*) *schmeichelnd*
handkerchief ['hæŋkətʃɪf] *Halstuch*
will go *hier: kannst du ... haben*
take off *abnehmen*
art [ɑːt] = are
rickety ['rɪkɪtɪ] *wack(e)lig, baufällig*
agile ['ædʒaɪl] *flink, behend(e)*

---

mounted ['maʊntɪd] *hier: im Sattel saß*

---

oaken frame ['əʊkən freɪm] *Eichengestell*
torn [tɔːn] *von* tear [teə] *zerreißen; hier: zerschlissen*

the °tooled leather band, and she reached up and °knotted the green silk handkerchief about his neck. Pepé's blue °denim coat was much darker than his °jeans, for it had been washed much less often.

Mama handed up the big medicine bottle and the silver coins. "That for the medicine," she said, "and that for the salt. That for a candle to burn for the papa. That for °*dulces* for the little ones. Our friend Mrs. Rodriguez will give you dinner and maybe a bed for the night. When you go to the church say only ten °Paternosters and only twenty-five Ave Marias. Oh! I know, big coyote. You would sit there °flapping your mouth over Aves all day while you looked at the candles and the holy pictures. That is not good °devotion to stare at the pretty things."

The black hat, covering the high pointed head and black °thatched hair of Pepé, °gave him °dignity and age. He °sat the °rangy horse well. Mama thought how handsome he was, dark and lean and tall. "I would not send thee now alone, thou little one, except for the medicine," she said softly. "It is not good to have no medicine, for who knows when the toothache will come, or the °sadness of the stomach. These things are."

°"Adios, Mama," Pepé cried. "I will come back soon. You may send me often alone. I am a man."

"Thou art a foolish chicken."

He °straightened his shoulders, °flipped the °reins against the horse's shoulder and rode away. He turned

---

tooled [tu:ld] *verziehrt*
knot [nɔt] *knoten, knüpfen*

denim ['denim] *grober Baumwolldrillich*
jeans Pl [dʒi:nz] *Jeans, Niethose*

dulces Pl ['dulθez] (Span.) *Süßigkeiten*

Paternoster ['pætə'nɔstə] *Vaterunser*

flapping your mouth over Aves ['ɑ:viz] *hier: die Ave Marias mechanisch herunterleiern*
devotion [di'vəuʃən] *Andacht, Frömmigkeit*

thatched hair [θætʃt hɛə] *Haarwald,-dach*
gave him [geiv] *verlieh ihm*
dignity ['digniti] *Würde*
sat the horse well *von* sit a horse well *gut zu Pferde sitzen*
rangy AE ['reindʒi] *geschmeidig; langglied(e)rig*

sadness of the stomach ['sædnis, 'stʌmək] *Magen-, Leibschmerzen*
adios [ædi'əus] *lebe wohl!*

straighten ['streitn] *hier: straffen*
flip *leicht schlagen*
reins Pl [reinz] *Zügel*

17

once and saw that they still watched him, Emilio and Rosy and Mama. Pepé grinned with pride and gladness and °lifted the °tough °buckskin horse to a trot.

When he had °dropped out of sight over a little dip in the road, Mama turned to the black ones, but she spoke to herself. "He is nearly a man now," she said. "It will be a nice thing to have a man in the house again." Her eyes °sharpened on the children. "Go to the rocks now. The °tide is going out. There will be °abalones to be found." She put the iron °hooks into their hands and °saw them down the °steep °trail to the reefs. She brought the smooth stone °*metate* to the doorway and sat °grinding her corn to °flour and looking occasionally at the road over which Pepé had gone. The °noonday came and then the afternoon, when the little ones beat the abalones on a rock to make them °tender and Mama °patted the °tortillas to make them thin. They ate their dinner as the red sun was °plunging down toward the ocean. They sat on the doorsteps and watched the big white moon come over the mountain °tops.

Mama said, "He is now at the house of our friend Mrs. Rodriguez. She will give him nice things to eat and maybe a present."

Emilio said, "Some day I too will ride to Monterey for medicine. Did Pepé °come to be a man today?"

Mama said wisely, "A boy gets to be a man when a man is needed. Remember this thing. I have known

lift to a trot [trɔt] *hier: in Trab setzen*

tough [tʌf] *zäh*
buckskin horse ['bʌkskin] *Falbe, gelbbraunes Pferd*
drop out of sight over a little dip [sait] *hinter e-r kleinen (Boden)Senke verschwinden*

sharpen on ['ʃɑːpən] *hier: sich scharf richten auf*
tide [taid] *Gezeiten, Ebbe u. Flut*
the tide is going out *die Flut fällt*
abalone AE [æbə'ləuni] *See-, Meerohr, Ohrschnecke*
hook [huk] *Haken*
saw s.o. to [sɔː] *von see s.o. to [siː] j-n begleiten nach od. zu*
steep [stiːp] *steil*
trail [treil] *(Trampel)Pfad*
metate [mə'tɑːdi] *(Span.) Mahlstein*
grind [graind] *(zer)mahlen, zerreiben*
flour ['flauə] *Mehl*
noonday ['nuːndei] *Mittag (-szeit)*
tender ['tendə] *zart, weich*
pat [pæt] *klopfen*
tortilla [tɔr'tilja] *(Span.) Tortilla, Maisfladen*
plunge down toward [plʌndʒ, tə'wɔːd] *hier: hinabgleiten zu*
top [tɔp] *Gipfel, Spitze*

come to be *werden*

boys forty years old because there was no need for a man."

Soon afterwards they °retired, Mama in her big oak bed on one side of the room, Emilio and Rosy in their boxes full of straw and °sheepskins on the other side of the room.

The moon went over the sky and the surf °roared on the rocks. The °roosters °crowed the first call. The surf °subsided to a °whispering °surge against the reef. The moon dropped toward the sea. The roosters crowed again.

The moon was °near down to the water when Pepé rode on a °winded horse to his home °flat. His dog °bounced out and °circled the horse °yelping with pleasure. Pepé °slid off the saddle to the ground. The °weathered little shack was silver in the moonlight and the square shadow of it was black to the north and east. Against the east the °piling mountains were °misty with light; their tops °melted into the sky.

Pepé walked °wearily up the three steps and into the house. It was dark inside. There was a °rustle in the corner.

Mama cried out from her bed, °"Who comes? Pepé, is it thou?"

"Sí, Mama."

"Did you get the medicine?"

"Sí, Mama."

"Well, go to sleep, then. I thought you would be sleeping at the house of Mrs. Rodriguez." Pepé stood silently in the dark room. "Why do you stand there, Pepé? Did you drink wine?"

retire [ri'taiə] *sich zur Ruhe begeben, zu Bett gehen*

sheepskin ['ʃiːpskin] *Schaffell*

roar [rɔː] *tosen, toben*
rooster ['ruːstə] *(Haus)Hahn*
crow [krəu] *krähen*
subside to [səb'said] *hier: verebben zu*
whispering ['wispəriŋ] *raunend, flüsternd*
surge [səːdʒ] *Woge, Welle*

near [niə] = almost

winded ['windid] *erschöpft, außer Atem*
flat [flæt] *Ebene; Flachland*
bounce out [bauns] *herausspringen*
circle ['səːkl] *umkreisen*
yelp [jelp] *kläffen, jaulen*
slid off *von* slide off [slaid] *gleiten aus* od. *von*
weathered ['weðəd] *vom Wetter mitgenommen, verwittert*
piling ['pailiŋ] *hier: hoch aufragend*
misty ['misti] *dunstig*
melt into *verschmelzen mit*
weary ['wiəri] *müde, erschöpft*

rustle ['rʌsl] *Rascheln*

who comes? = who is there?

"*Sí*, Mama."

"Well, go to bed then and sleep out the wine."

His voice was tired and patient, but very °firm. °"Light the candle, Mama. I must go away into the mountains."

"What is this, Pepé? You are crazy." Mama °struck a °sulphur match and held the little blue °burr until the flame spread up the stick. She °set light to the candle on the floor beside her bed. "Now, Pepé, what is this you say?" She looked °anxiously into his face.

He was changed. The °fragile °quality seemed to have gone from his chin. His mouth was less full than it had been, the lines of the lips were straighter, but in his eyes the greatest change had taken place. There was no laughter in them any more, nor any °bashfulness. They were °sharp and °bright and °purposeful.

He told her °in a tired monotone, told her everything just as it had happened. A few people came into the kitchen of Mrs. Rodriguez. There was wine to drink. Pepé drank wine. The little °quarrel—the man °started toward Pepé and then the knife—it went almost by itself. It flew, it °darted before Pepé knew it. As he talked, Mama's face grew °stern, and it seemed to grow more lean. Pepé finished. "I am a man now, Mama. The man said names to me I could not allow."

Mama °nodded. "Yes, thou art a man, my poor little Pepé. Thou art a man. I have seen it °coming on thee. I have watched you throwing the knife into the post, and I have been afraid."

firm [fəːm] *fest, entschlossen*
light [lait] *anzünden*

struck [strʌk] *von* strike [straik] *ent-, anzünden*
sulphur match [ˈsʌlfə mætʃ] *Schwefelholz*
burr [bəː] *Ring*
set light to *anzünden*

anxious [ˈæŋkʃəs] *besorgt*

quality [ˈkwɔliti] *Eigenschaft; Beschaffenheit*
fragile quality *hier: Zartheit, alles Zarte*

bashfulness [ˈbæʃfulnis] *Schüchternheit, Scheu*
sharp [ʃɑːp] *wachsam, scharf*
bright [brait] *intelligent, wach*
purposeful [ˈpəːpəsful] *entschlossen, zielbewußt*
in a monotone [ˈmɔnətəun] *hier: mit monotoner Stimme*

quarrel [ˈkwɔrəl] *Streit*
start toward s.o. [stɑːt] *auf j-n losgehen*
dart [dɑːt] *sausen, schießen, hier: durch die Luft schießen*
stern [stəːn] *streng, hart*

nod [nɔd] *nicken*

come on s.o. *j-m zustoßen*

20

For a moment her face had °softened, but now it grew stern again. "Come! We must get you ready. Go. Awaken Emilio and Rosy. Go quickly."

Pepé °stepped over to the corner where his brother and sister slept among the sheepskins. He °leaned down and shook them gently. "Come, Rosy! Come, Emilio! The mama says you must °arise."

The little black ones °sat up and rubbed their eyes in the candlelight. Mama was out of bed now, her long black skirt over her nightgown. "Emilio," she cried. "Go up and catch the other horse for Pepé. Quickly, now! Quickly." Emilio put his legs in his °overalls and °stumbled sleepily out the door.

"You heard no one behind you on the road?" Mama °demanded.

"No, Mama. I listened carefully. No one was on the road."

Mama darted like a bird about the room. From a nail on the wall she took a °canvas water bag and threw it on the floor. She °stripped a blanket from her bed and rolled it into a °tight °tube and tied the ends with string. From a box beside the °stove she lifted a flour sack half full of black °stringy °jerky. "Your father's black coat, Pepé. Here, °put it on."

Pepé stood in the middle of the floor watching her °activity. She reached behind the door and brought out the °rifle, °a long 38–56, worn shiny the whole length of the °barrel. Pepé took it from her and held it in the °crook of his elbow. Mama brought

---

soften ['sɔfn] *weich(er)* od. *sanft(er) werden*

step over to *hinübergehen zu*

lean down [liːn] *sich hinunter-beugen*

arise AE [ə'raiz] *aufstehen, sich erheben*
sat up *von* sit up *sich (im Bett) aufrichten*

overalls *Pl* ['əuvərɔːlz] *Arbeits-hose, Overall*
stumble ['stʌmbl] *stolpern, taumeln*

demand [di'mɑːnd] *gebiete-risch fragen*

canvas ['kænvəs] *Segeltuch; aus Segeltuch*
water bag *Wassersack*
strip *wegnehmen, entfernen*
tight [tait] *straff, fest, eng*
tube [tjuːb] *Röhre, Schlauch*
stove [stəuv] *Ofen, Herd*
stringy ['striŋi] *in Streifen ge-schnitten*
jerky ['dʒəːki] *Dörrfleisch (be-sonders vom Rind)*
put on *anziehen*
activity [æk'tiviti] *Tätigkeit; Betriebsamkeit*
rifle ['raifl] *Gewehr, Büchse*
a long 38–56 *ein 38–56 Lang-lauf(gewehr)*
barrel ['bærəl] *(Gewehr)Lauf*

crook of the elbow [kruk, 'elbəu] *Armbeuge*

21

a little leather bag and counted the °cartridges into his hand. °"Only ten °left," she warned. "You must not °waste them."

Emilio °put his head in the door. °"'*Qui 'st 'l caballo*, Mama."

"Put on the saddle from the other horse. Tie on the blanket. Here, tie the jerky to the °saddle horn."

Still Pepé stood silently watching his mother's °frantic activity. His chin looked hard, and his sweet mouth was °drawn and thin. His little eyes followed Mama about the room almost °suspiciously.

Rosy asked softly, °"Where goes Pepé?"

Mama's eyes were °fierce. "Pepé goes on a journey. Pepé is a man now. He has a man's thing to do."

Pepé straightened his shoulders. His mouth changed until he looked very much like Mama.

At last the °preparation was finished. The loaded horse stood outside the door. The water bag °dripped a line of °moisture down the °bay shoulder.

The moonlight °was being thinned by the dawn and the big white moon was near down to the sea. The family stood by the shack. Mama °confronted Pepé. "Look, my son! Do not stop until it is dark again. Do not sleep even though you are tired. Take care of the horse °in order that he may not stop °of weariness. Remember to be careful with the °bullets—there are only ten. Do not fill thy °stomach with jerky or °it will make thee sick. Eat a little jerky and fill thy stomach with

cartridge ['kɑːtridʒ] *Patrone*

left = be left *übrigbleiben, übrig sein*
only ten left *hier: es sind nur noch zehn da*
waste [weist] *verschwenden*
put in *hereinstecken*
'Qui 'st 'l caballo ['kistl ka'baljɔ] (*Span.*) *Hier ist das Pferd*
saddle horn ['sædl hɔːn] *hornförmige Verlängerung des Sattelknaufes beim amerikanischen Cowboysattel*
frantic ['fræntik] *verzweifelt, wild*
drawn [drɔːn] *verkniffen*

suspicious [səs'piʃəs] *mißtrauisch, argwöhnisch*
where goes ... ? = where does ... go?
fierce [fiəs] *wild, wütend, grimmig*

preparation [prepə'reiʃən] *Vorbereitung*
drip (*herab)tropfen lassen*
moisture ['mɔistʃə] *Feuchtigkeit*
... dripped a line of moisture down ... *vom ... tropfte es in e-m feuchten Streifen ... herunter*
bay [bei] *rotbraun*
was being thinned by the dawn [θind, dɔːn] *wurde durch die Morgendämmerung fahl(er)*
confront [kən'frʌnt] *gegenübertreten, -stehen, hier: vor (j-m) stehen*

in order that ['ɔːdə] *damit*

of weariness ['wiərinis] *aus od. vor Müdigkeit*
bullet ['bulit] *Kugel*
stomach *Magen; Bauch*
it makes s.o. sick *j-m wird übel od. schlecht davon*

grass. When thou °comest to the high mountains, if thou °seest any of the dark watching men, go not near to them nor try to speak to them. And forget not thy °prayers." She put her lean hands on Pepé's shoulders, stood on her toes and kissed him formally on both cheeks, and Pepé kissed her on both cheeks. Then he went to Emilio and Rosy and kissed both of their cheeks.

Pepé turned back to Mama. He seemed to look for a little °softness, a little °weakness in her. His eyes were searching, but Mama's face °remained fierce. "Go now," she said. "Do not wait to be °caught like a chicken."

Pepé pulled himself into the saddle. "I am a man," he said.

It was the first °dawn when he rode up the hill toward the little °canyon °which let a trail into the mountains. Moonlight and daylight fought with each other, and the two °warring qualities made it difficult to see. Before Pepé had gone a hundred °yards, the °outlines of his figure were °misty; and long before he entered the canyon, he had become a grey, °indefinite shadow.

Mama stood stiffly in front of her doorstep, and on either side of her stood Emilio and Rosy. They °cast °furtive °glances at Mama °now and then.

When the grey °shape of Pepé melted into the °hillside and disappeared, Mama °relaxed. She began the high, °whining °keen of the °death wail. "Our beautiful—our brave," she cried.

"Our °protector, our son is gone." Emilio and Rosy °moaned beside her. "Our beautiful—our brave, he is gone." It was the °formal wail. It rose to a high °piercing °whine and °subsided to a moan. Mama raised it three times and then she turned and went into the house and shut the door.

Emilio and Rosy stood wondering in the dawn. They heard Mama °whimpering in the house. They went out to sit on the cliff above the ocean. They touched shoulders. "When did Pepé come to be a man?" Emilio asked.

"Last night," said Rosy. "Last night in Monterey." °The ocean clouds °turned red with the sun that was behind the mountains.

"We will have no breakfast," said Emilio. "Mama will not want to cook." Rosy did not answer him. "Where is Pepé gone?" he asked.

Rosy looked around at him. She °drew her °knowledge from the quiet air. "He has gone on a journey. He will never come back."

"Is he dead? Do you think he is dead?"

Rosy looked back at the ocean again. A little °steamer, °drawing a °line of smoke, sat on the edge of the horizon. "He is not dead," Rosy explained. "Not yet."

Pepé °rested the big rifle across the saddle in front of him. He let the horse walk up the hill and he didn't look back. The stony slope took on a °coat of short brush so that Pepé found the entrance to a trail and entered it.

---

protector [prə'tektə] *Beschützer*

moan [məun] *(weh)klagen, jammern, stöhnen*

formal ['fɔːməl] *konventionell, hier: überliefert*

piercing ['pɪəsɪŋ] *durchdringend*

whine [waɪn] *Gejammer*

subside to a moan *hier: in ein Stöhnen übergehen*

whimper ['wɪmpə] *wimmern*

the ocean clouds *Pl* ['əuʃən klaudz] *die Wolken über dem Meer*

turn red [tɜːn] *rot werden, sich rot verfärben*

drew from [druː] *von* draw from [drɔː] *hier: beziehen aus*

knowledge ['nɔlɪdʒ] *Kenntnis, Wissen, hier: Weisheit*

steamer ['stiːmə] *Dampfer*

draw [drɔː] *ziehen, hier: hinter sich herziehen*

line of smoke [sməuk] *Rauchfahne*

rest *legen*

coat [kəut] *Schicht*

When he came to the canyon °opening, he °swung once in his saddle and looked back, but the houses were °swallowed in the misty light. Pepé °jerked forward again. The high °shoulder of the canyon °closed in on him. His horse stretched out its neck and sighed and °settled to the trail.

It was a °well-worn path, dark soft °leaf-mould earth °strewn with broken pieces of °sandstone. The trail °rounded the shoulder of the canyon and °dropped steeply into the bed of the stream. In the °shallows the water °ran smoothly, glinting in the first morning sun. Small round stones on the bottom were as brown as rust with °sun moss. In the sand along the edges of the stream the tall, rich wild °mint grew, while in the water itself the °cress, old and tough, °had gone to °heavy seed.

The path went into the stream and °emerged on the other side. The horse °sloshed into the water and stopped. Pepé °dropped his °bridle and let the beast drink of the running water.

Soon the canyon sides became steep and the first °giant °sentinel redwoods °guarded the trail, great round red °trunks bearing °foliage as green and °lacy as °ferns. Once Pepé was among the trees, the sun was lost. A °perfumed and °purple light lay in the °pale green of the °underbrush. °Gooseberry °bushes and °blackberries and tall ferns °lined the stream, and °overhead the branches of the redwoods met and °cut off the sky.

opening [ˈəupniŋ] *Öffnung*
swung [swʌŋ] = swung round
 *von* swing round [swiŋ] *sich ruckartig umdrehen*
swallow [ˈswɔləu] (*ver*)*schlucken*
jerk [dʒəːk] *schnellen, hier: sich mit e-m Ruck drehen*
shoulder [ˈʃəuldə] *hier:* (*Fels-*)*Vorsprung*
close in on [kləuz] *sich heranarbeiten an, hier: einschließen*
settle to [ˈsetl] *hier: folgen*
well-worn [ˈwelˈwɔːn] *ausgetreten, viel benutzt*
leaf-mould earth [ˈliːfməuld, əːθ] = leaf mould *Lauberde*
strewn [struːn] *von* strew [struː] *bestreuen, hier: hier u. da bedecken*
sandstone [ˈsændstəun] *Sandstein*
round [raund] *biegen um*
drop into *hier: hinunterführen zu*
shallow [ˈʃæləu] *seichte Stelle, Untiefe*
ran smoothly [ˈsmuːðli] *von* run smoothly *ruhig dahinfließen*
sun moss [mɔs] *Wasserportulak*
mint *Minze*
cress [kres] *Kresse*
had gone to seed [gɔn, siːd] *von* go to seed *in Samen schießen*
heavy [ˈhevi] *stark, heftig*
emerge [iˈməːdʒ] *herauskommen*
slosh [slɔʃ] *patschen*
drop *fallen lassen*
bridle [ˈbraidl] *Zügel; Zaum* (*-zeug*)
giant [ˈdʒaiənt] *riesig, Riesen...*
sentinel [ˈsentinl] *Schildwache, hier:* = ... guarded the trail like sentinels
guard [gɑːd] *sichern, schützen, bewachen*
trunk [trʌŋk] (*Baum*)*Stamm*
foliage [ˈfəuliidʒ] *Blätter*
lacy [ˈleisi] *spitzenartig*
fern [fəːn] *Farn*(*kraut*)
perfumed [ˈpəːfjuːmd] *dufterfüllt*

Pepé drank from the water bag, and he reached into the flour sack and brought out a black °string of jerky. His white teeth °gnawed at the string until the tough meat parted. He chewed slowly and drank occasionally from the water bag. His little eyes were °slumberous and tired, but the muscles of his face were °hard set. The earth of the trail was black now. It gave up a hollow sound under the walking °hoofbeats.

The stream fell more sharply. Little waterfalls °splashed on the stones. Five-fingered ferns hung over the water and °dripped °spray from their fingertips. Pepé rode °half over in his saddle, °dangling one leg °loosely. He picked a °bay leaf from a tree beside the way and put it into his mouth for a moment to °flavor the dry jerky. He held the gun loosely across the °pommel.

Suddenly he °squared in his saddle, swung the horse from the trail and °kicked it hurriedly up behind a big redwood tree. He pulled up the reins tight against the °bit to °keep the horse from °whinnying. His face was °intent and his °nostrils quivered a little.

A hollow °pounding came down the trail, and a °horseman rode by, a fat man with red cheeks and a white °stubble beard. His horse put down its head and °blubbered at the trail when it came to the place where Pepé had °turned off. °"Hold up!" said the man and he pulled up his horse's head.

When the last sound of the °hooves died away, Pepé came back into the trail again. He did not relax in the

purple ['pəːpl] *purpurrot*
pale [peil] *fahl, blaß*
underbrush ['ʌndəbrʌʃ] *Unterholz*
gooseberry ['guzbəri] *Stachelbeere*
bush [buʃ] *Strauch*
blackberry ['blækbəri] *Brombeere*
line [lain] *säumen*
overhead ['əuvə'hed] *oben*
cut off *hier: aussperren*

---

string [striŋ] *hier: dünner Streifen*
gnaw at [nɔː] *nagen an*
slumberous ['slʌmbərəs] *schläfrig*
be hard set *hier: angespannt sein*
hoofbeat ['huːfbiːt] *Hufschlag*
splash [splæʃ] *spritzen*
drip *tropfen lassen, hier: (ver-)sprühen*
spray [sprei] *hier: feiner Regen*
half over *hier: vornübergebeugt*
dangle ['dæŋgl] *baumeln lassen*
loose [luːs] *lose, frei; locker*
bay [bei] *Lorbeer(baum)*
flavor AE = flavour BE ['fleivə] *würzen, hier: Geschmack geben*
pommel ['pʌml] *Sattelknauf*
square [skwɛə] *hier: sich straff od. gerade aufrichten*
kick *hier: treiben*
bit *Gebiß (am Pferdezaum)*
keep s.o. from doing s.th. *j-n davon abhalten, et. zu tun*
whinny ['wini] *wiehern*
intent [in'tent] *aufmerksam, gespannt, konzentriert*
nostril ['nɔstril] *Nasenloch; Nüster*
pounding ['paundiŋ] *Stampfen*
horseman ['hɔːsmən] *Reiter*
stubble beard ['stʌbl biəd] *Stoppelbart*
blubber ['blʌbə] *hier: schnauben*
turn off *abbiegen*
hold up [həuld] *(Kopf) hoch!*

hoof [huːf] *Huf*

26

saddle any more. He lifted the big rifle and °swung the lever to throw a °shell into the °chamber, and then he let down the °hammer to °half cock.

The trail grew very steep. Now the redwood trees were smaller and their tops were dead, °bitten dead where the wind reached them. The horse °plodded on; the sun went slowly overhead and started down toward the afternoon.

Where the stream came out of a side canyon, the trail left it. Pepé °dismounted and °watered his horse and °filled up his water bag. As soon as the trail had parted from the stream, the trees were gone and only the thick °brittle °sage and °manzanita and °chaparral °edged the trail. And the soft black earth was gone, too, leaving only the light °tan broken rock for the trail bed. °Lizards °scampered away into the brush as the horse rattled over the little stones.

Pepé turned in his saddle and looked back. He was °in the open now: he could be seen from a distance. As he °ascended the trail the country grew more rough and terrible and dry. The way wound about the bases of great square rocks. Little grey rabbits °skittered in the brush. A bird °made a °monotonous high °creaking. Eastward the bare rock mountaintops were pale and powder-dry under the °dropping sun. The horse °plodded up and up the trail toward a little V in the °ridge which was the °pass.

Pepé looked suspiciously back every minute or so, and his eyes °sought the

swung the lever [swʌŋ, ˈliːvə] *von* swing the lever *den Verschluß öffnen*
shell AE [ʃel] *Patrone*
chamber [ˈtʃeimbə] *(Gewehr-) Kammer*
hammer [ˈhæmə] *Hahn (e-r Feuerwaffe)*
half cock [kɔk] *Vorderrast (= halbgespannter Hahn, so daß die Waffe noch gesichert ist)*
bitten dead [ded] *hier: abgestorben*
plod on [plɔd] *weiterstapfen*
dismount [disˈmaunt] *absteigen, absitzen*
water [ˈwɔːtə] *tränken*
fill up *vollfüllen*

brittle [ˈbritl] *spröde*
sage [seidʒ] *Salbei*
manzanita [mænzəˈniːtə] *amerikanische Bärentraube*
chaparral [tʃæpəˈræl] *Chaparral (immergrünes Gebüsch)*
edge [edʒ] *einfassen, begrenzen*
tan [tæn] *gelbbraun, lohfarben*
lizard [ˈlizəd] *Eidechse*
scamper away [ˈskæmpə] *sich davonmachen*

in the open [ˈəupən] *im Freien*

ascend [əˈsend] *hier: hinaufreiten*
skitter AE [ˈskitə] *hüpfen, huschen*
made [meid] *von* make [meik] *hier: von sich geben*
monotonous [məˈnɔtnəs] *monoton, eintönig*
creaking [ˈkriːkiŋ] *Kreischen*
dropping *sinkend*
plod up and up *immer weiter bergauf stapfen*
ridge [ridʒ] *(Gebirgs)Kamm, Grat*
pass [pɑːs] *Paß, Joch, (Berg-) Sattel*
sought [sɔːt] *von* seek [siːk] *absuchen*

tops of the ridges ahead. Once, on a white °barren °spur, he saw a black figure for a moment, but he looked quickly away, for it was one of the dark watchers. No one knew who the watchers were, nor where they lived, but it was better to °ignore them and never to show interest in them. They did not °bother one who stayed on the trail and °minded his own business.

The air was °parched and full of light dust blown by the °breeze from the °eroding mountains. Pepé drank °sparingly from his bag and °corked it tightly and hung it on the horn again. The trail moved up the dry °shale hillside, °avoiding rocks, dropping under °clefts, climbing in and out of old °water scars. When he arrived at the little pass he stopped and looked back for a long time. No dark watchers were to be seen now. The trail behind was empty. Only the high tops of the redwoods °indicated where the stream flowed.

Pepé rode on through the pass. His little eyes were nearly closed with weariness, but his face was stern, °relentless and manly. The high mountain wind °coasted sighing through the pass and whistled on the edges of the big blocks of broken granite. In the air, a °red-tailed hawk sailed over close to the ridge and screamed angrily. Pepé went slowly through the broken °jagged pass and looked down on the other side.

The trail dropped quickly, °staggering among °broken rock. At the bottom of the slope there was a dark

barren ['bærən] *kahl, öde*
spur [spə:] *Ausläufer, Vorsprung*

ignore [ig'nɔ:] *ignorieren, nicht beachten*

bother ['bɔðə] *belästigen*

mind one's own business [maind, əun, 'biznis] *sich um s-e eigenen Sachen kümmern*
parched [pɑ:tʃt] *ausgedörrt, hier: trocken*
breeze [bri:z] *Brise, leichter Wind*
eroding [i'rəudiŋ] *mürbe, zerfallend*
sparing ['speəriŋ] *sparsam, wenig*
cork [kɔ:k] *zu-, verkorken*
shale [ʃeil] *Schiefer*
avoid [ə'vɔid] *ausreichen, meiden*
cleft [kleft] *Felsspalte*
water scar [skɑ:] *hier: Wasserrinne*
indicate ['indikeit] *(an)zeigen, verraten*

relentless [ri'lentlis] *unbarmherzig, hier: hart*
coast [kəust] *sich ohne Anstrengung fortbewegen, hier: streichen*

red-tailed hawk [hɔ:k] *Rotschwanzbussard*

jagged ['dʒægid] *schroff, zerklüftet*

stagger ['stægə] *(sch)wanken, taumeln, hier: sich mühsam e-n Weg suchen*
broken rock ['brəukən] *zerklüftete Felsen*

°crease, °thick with brush, and on the other side of the crease a little flat, in which a °grove of °oak trees grew. A °scar of green grass °cut across the flat. And behind the flat another mountain rose, °desolate with dead rocks and °starving little black bushes. Pepé drank from the bag again for the air was so dry that it °encrusted his nostrils and burned his lips. He put the horse down the trail. The hooves °slipped and °struggled on the steep way, °starting little stones that rolled off into the brush. The sun was gone behind the westward mountain now, but still it glowed °brilliantly on the oaks and on the grassy flat. The rocks and the hillsides still sent up waves of the heat they had gathered from the day's sun.

Pepé looked up to the top of the next dry °withered ridge. He saw a dark form against the sky, a man's figure standing on top of a rock, and he glanced away quickly not to appear curious. When a moment later he looked up again, the figure was gone.

Downward the trail was quickly °covered. Sometimes the horse °floundered for °footing, sometimes °set his feet and °slid a little way. They came at last to the bottom where the dark chaparral was higher than Pepé's head. He held up his rifle on one side and his arm on the other to °shield his face from the sharp brittle fingers of the brush.

Up and out of the crease he rode, and up a little cliff. The grassy flat was before him, and the round °comfortable oaks. For a moment he studied the

crease [kri:s] *Falte*
thick with [θik] *über u. über bedeckt von, voll von*
grove [grəuv] *Hain, Wäldchen*
oak (tree) [əuk] *Eiche*
scar of ... grass *Grasnarbe*
cut across (*quer*) *durchschneiden,* (*quer*) (*hindurch*)*gehen durch*
desolate ['desəlit] *trostlos*
starving ['stɑ:viŋ] *verkümmert*
encrust [in'krʌst] *verkrusten*

slip *ausgleiten, -rutschen*
struggle ['strʌgl] *sich (ab-) mühen, sich anstrengen* od. *quälen*
start [stɑ:t] *in Bewegung setzen*

brilliant ['briljənt] *leuchtend, hell*

withered ['wiðəd] *verdorrt, hier: kahl*

cover ['kʌvə] *zurücklegen (Strecke)*
flounder ['flaundə] *zappeln, hier: den Boden abtasten*
footing ['futiŋ] *Halt, Stand*
set his feet *hier: seine Beine steif machen*
slid *von* slide *rutschen, gleiten*

shield [ʃi:ld] *schützen*

comfortable ['kʌmfətəbl] *wohltuend; tröstlich*

trail down which he had come, but there was no movement and no sound from it. Finally he rode out over the flat, to the green °streak, and at the upper end of the °damp he found a little °spring °welling out of the earth and °dropping into a °dug basin before it °seeped out over the flat.

Pepé filled his bag first, and then he let the thirsty horse drink out of the °pool. He led the horse to the °clump of oaks, and in the middle of the grove, °fairly protected from sight on all sides, he °took off the saddle and the bridle and laid them on the ground. The horse stretched his °jaws sideways and °yawned. Pepé knotted the °lead rope about the horse's neck and tied him to a °sapling among the oaks, where he could °graze in a fairly large circle.

When the horse was gnawing hungrily at the dry grass, Pepé went to the saddle and took a black string of jerky from the sack and °strolled to an oak tree on the edge of the grove, from under which he could watch the trail. He sat down in the °crisp dry oak leaves and automatically felt for his big black knife to cut the jerky, but he had no knife. He leaned back on his elbow and gnawed at the tough strong meat. His face was °blank, but it was a man's face.

The bright evening light °washed the eastern ridge, but the valley was darkening. °Doves flew down from the hills to the spring, and the °quail came running out of the brush and °joined them, calling clearly to one another.

streak [striːk] *Streifen*

damp [dæmp] *Feuchtigkeit, hier: feuchte Stelle*
spring [spriŋ] *Quelle*
well out *hervorsprudeln, -quellen*
drop *(herab)tropfen*
dug basin [dʌg ˈbeisn] *ausgegrabenes Becken*
seep out [siːp] *heraussickern*
pool [puːl] *Lache, Pfütze, Wasserloch*
clump [klʌmp] *Gruppe (Bäume)*
fairly [ˈfɛəli] *ziemlich; leidlich*
take off the bridle [tuk] *von take off the bridle abzäumen*

jaw [dʒɔː] *Kinnbacken, Kinnladen, Kiefer*
yawn [jɔːn] *gähnen*
lead rope [liːd rəup] *(richtungweisender) Zügel*
sapling [ˈsæpliŋ] *junger Baum*
graze [greiz] *grasen, weiden*

stroll [strəul] *schlendern*

crisp [krisp] *knusp(e)rig, hier: knisternd, raschelnd*

blank [blæŋk] *ausdruckslos*

wash [wɔʃ] *mit Farbe überziehen*

dove [dʌv] *Taube*

quail [kweil] *Wachtel*

join [dʒɔin] *sich gesellen zu*

Out of the corner of his eye Pepé saw a shadow grow out of the °bushy crease. He turned his head slowly. A big °spotted °wildcat was °creeping toward the spring, °belly to the ground, °moving like thought.

Pepé °cocked his rifle and °edged the °muzzle slowly around. Then he looked °apprehensively up the trail and dropped the hammer again. From the ground beside him he °picked an oak °twig and threw it toward the spring. The quail flew up with a °roar and the doves °whistled away. The big cat stood up: for a long moment he looked at Pepé with cold yellow eyes, and then fearlessly walked back into the °gulch.

The °dusk gathered quickly in the deep valley. Pepé °muttered his prayers, put his head down on his arm and went instantly to sleep.

The moon came up and filled the valley with cold blue light, and the wind swept °rustling down from the peaks. The °owls °worked up and down the slopes looking for rabbits. Down in the brush of the gulch a coyote °gabbled. The oak trees °whispered softly in the night breeze.

Pepé °started up, listening. His horse had whinnied. The moon was just slipping behind the western ridge, leaving the valley in darkness behind it. Pepé sat tensely °gripping his rifle. From far up the trail he heard an answering °whinny and the °crash of °shod hooves on the broken rock. He jumped to his feet, ran to his horse and led it under the trees. He threw on the saddle and °cinched it tight for

bushy ['buʃi] *mit Sträuchern bewachsen*

spotted ['spɔtid] *gefleckt; getigert*
wildcat ['waildkæt] *Wildkatze*
creep [kriːp] *kriechen, schleichen*
belly ['beli] *Bauch*
moving like thought ['muːviŋ, θɔːt] *hier: lautlos wie ein Gedanke (sich bewegend)*
cock [kɔk] *spannen (Gewehrhahn)*
edge [edʒ] *schieben, bewegen*
muzzle ['mʌzl] *Mündung*
apprehensive [æpri'hensiv] *besorgt, ängstlich*
pick *auflesen, sammeln, hier: nehmen*
twig [twig] *(dünner) Zweig, kleiner Ast*
roar [rɔː] *Geschrei, Lärm*
whistle away AE = whistle off BE ['wisl] *sich aus dem Staube machen*
gulch AE [gʌlʃ] *(Berg)Schlucht*
dusk [dʌsk] *(Abend)Dämmerung*
mutter ['mʌtə] *murmeln*

rustle ['rʌsl] *rauschen, rascheln*
owl [aul] *Eule*
work up and down *hier: abfliegen*
gabble ['gæbl] *schwatzen*
whisper ['wispə] *raunen, flüstern*

start up *auffahren, hochschrecken*

grip *umklammern, (fest)halten*

whinny ['wini] *Wiehern*
crash [kræʃ] *Krach(en), hier: Geräusch*
shod [ʃɔd] *beschlagen*

cinch AE [sintʃ] *(fest)schnallen*

the steep trail, caught the unwilling head and forced the bit into the mouth. He felt the saddle to make sure the water bag and the sack of jerky were there. Then he °mounted and turned up the hill.

mount [maunt] *aufs Pferd steigen, aufsitzen*

It was °velvet dark. The horse found the entrance to the trail where it left the flat, and started up, stumbling and slipping on the rocks. Pepé's hand rose up to his head. His hat was gone. He had left it under the oak tree.

velvet ['velvit] *samten, aus Samt*

The horse had struggled far up the trail when the first change of dawn came into the air, a °steel greyness as light mixed thoroughly with dark. Gradually the sharp °snaggled edge of the ridge °stood out above them, °rotten granite °tortured and °eaten by the winds of time. Pepé had dropped his reins on the horn, leaving °direction to the horse. The brush °grabbed at his legs in the dark until one knee of his jeans was °ripped.

steel greyness [sti:l 'greinis] *stählernes Grau*

snaggled ['snægld] *unregelmäßig*
stood out *von* stand out *sich gut abheben*
rotten ['rɔtn] *morsch, mürbe*
torture ['tɔ:tʃə] *mißhandeln, foltern*
eaten ['i:tn] *von* eat [i:t] *zerfressen*
direction [di'rekʃən] *Richtung*
grab at [græb] *greifen nach*
rip *auf-, zerschlitzen*

Gradually the light flowed down over the ridge. The °starved brush and rocks stood out in the °half light, strange and °lonely in °high °perspective. Then there came °warmth into the light. Pepé °drew up and looked back, but he could see nothing in the darker valley below. The sky turned blue over the coming sun. In the °waste of the °mountainside, the poor dry brush grew only three feet high. Here and there, big °outcroppings of unrotted granite stood up like °mouldering houses. Pepé relaxed a little. He drank from his water bag and bit off a piece of

starved [stɑ:vd] *verkümmert*
half light *hier: dämm(e)riges Licht*
lonely ['ləunli] *hier: verloren*
high [hai] *hier: steil*
perspective [pə'spektiv] *Perspektive*
warmth [wɔ:mθ] *Wärme*
drew up [dru:] *von* draw up *(an)halten, stehenbleiben*
waste [weist] *Wüste, Öde; Geröll*
mountainside ['mauntinsaid] *Berghang*
outcropping ['autkrɔpiŋ] *zutage liegende Schicht*
mouldering ['məuldəriŋ] *zerfallend, zerbröckelnd, vermodernd*

erky. A single °eagle flew over, high in he light.

eagle ['iːgl] *Adler*

Without warning Pepé's horse screamed and fell on its side. He was almost °down before the °rifle crash °echoed up from the valley. From a hole behind the °struggling shoulder, a stream of bright °crimson blood °pumped and stopped and pumped and stopped. The hooves °threshed on the ground. Pepé lay half °stunned beside the horse. He looked slowly down the hill. A piece of sage °clipped off beside his head and another crash echoed up from side to side of the canyon. Pepé °flung himself frantically behind a bush.

be down *am Boden liegen*
rifle crash *hier:* (*Gewehr-*) *Schuß*
echo ['ekəu] *widerhallen*
echo up *herauftönen*
struggling *zappelnd*
crimson ['krimzn] *karmesin-, tiefrot*
pump [pʌmp] *pumpen*
thresh [θreʃ] *dreschen, hier: wild um sich schlagen*
stunned [stʌnd] *betäubt*
clipped off [klipt] *abgeschnitten werden*

flung [flʌŋ] *von* fling [fliŋ] *sich* (*herum*)*werfen*
crawl [krɔːl] *kriechen*

He °crawled up the hill on his knees and one hand. His right hand held the rifle up off the ground and pushed it ahead of him. He moved with the °instinctive °care of an animal. °Rapidly he °wormed his way toward one of the big outcroppings of granite on the hill above him. Where the brush was high he °doubled up and ran, but where the °cover was °slight he °wriggled forward on his stomach, pushing the rifle ahead of him. In the last little distance there was no cover at all. Pepé °poised and then he darted across the °space and °flashed around the corner of the rock.

instinctive [in'stiŋktiv] *instinktiv*
care [kɛə] *Vorsicht*
rapid ['ræpid] *schnell, rasch*
worm one's way [wəːm] *sich schlängeln*
double up ['dʌbl] *sich krümmen, hier: sich bücken*
cover ['kʌvə] *Deckung*
slight [slait] *gering(fügig)*
wriggle ['rigl] *sich winden* od. *schlängeln*

poise [pɔiz] *hier: regungslos u. angespannt verharren*
space [speis] *Stelle*
flash [flæʃ] *sich blitzschnell bewegen, hier: blitzschnell verschwinden*
pant [pænt] *keuchen*

He leaned °panting against the stone. When his breath came easier he moved along behind the big rock until he came to a narrow °split that °offered a thin °section of vision down the hill. Pepé lay on his stomach and pushed the rifle barrel through the °slit and waited.

split *Spalt*
offer ['ɔfə] (*an*)*bieten, hier: ermöglichen*
section of vision ['sekʃən, 'viʒən] *Blickwinkel*
slit *Schlitz, Spalt*

33

The sun °reddened the western ridges now. Already the °buzzards °were settling down toward the place where the horse lay. A small brown bird °scratchedʃ in the dead sage leaves directly in front of the rifle muzzle. The °coasting eagle flew back toward the rising sun.

Pepé saw a little movement in the brush far below. °His grip tightened on the gun. A little brown °doe stepped °daintily out on the trail and crossed it and disappeared into the brush again. For a long time Pepé waited. Far below he could see the little flat and the oak trees and the °slash of green. Suddenly his eyes °flashed back at the trail again. A quarter of a mile down there had been a quick movement in the chaparral. The rifle swung over. The °front sight °nestled in the V of the °rear sight. Pepé studied for a moment and then °raised the rear sight a °notch. The little movement in the brush came again. The °sight °settled on it. Pepé °squeezed the trigger. The explosion °crashed down the mountain and up the other side, and came °rattling back. The whole side of the slope grew still. No more movement. And then a white streak cut into the granite of the slit and °a bullet whined away and a crash °sounded up from below. Pepé felt a sharp °pain in his right hand. A °sliver of granite was °sticking out from between his first and second °knuckles and the point °protruded from his palm. Carefully he pulled out the sliver of stone. The wound bled °evenly and °gently. °No °vein nor °artery was cut.

redden ['redn] *rot färben*

buzzard ['bʌzəd] *Bussard*
were settling down toward the place where ... *hier: flogen dorthin, wo ...*
scratch [skrætʃ] *scharren*

coasting *dahinsegelnd, schwebend*

his grip tightened on the gun ['taitnd] *er packte* od. *hielt das Gewehr fester*
doe [dəu] *(Reh)Geiß*
dainty ['deinti] *zierlich, zart*

slash AE [slæʃ] *Sumpfgelände*
flash back at *hier: sich blitzschnell richten auf*

front sight [frʌnt sait] *Korn*
nestle ['nesl] *sich anschmiegen, hier: ruhen*
rear sight [riə] *Kimme*
raise [reiz] *hier: verstellen*
notch [nɔtʃ] *Kerbe, hier: Visiereinteilung*
sight *Visier*
settle on *hier: sich genau richten auf*
squeeze the trigger [skwi:z, 'trigə] *abdrücken*
crash *krachen; Krachen*
rattle ['rætl] *rattern, klappern*
a bullet whined away *hier: ein Querschläger surrte davon*
sound up [saund] *herauftönen*
pain [pein] *Schmerz(en Pl)*
sliver ['slivə] *Splitter*
stick out *herausstehen*
knuckle ['nʌkl] *Knöchel*
protrude [prə'tru:d] *herausragen, -treten*
even ['i:vən] *gleichmäßig*
gentle ['dʒentl] *leicht*
no ... nor [nɔ:] *weder ... noch*
vein [vein] *Vene*
artery ['ɑ:təri] *Arterie*

Pepé looked into a little dusty cave in the rock and °gathered a handful of °spider web, and he pressed the mass into the °cut, °plastering the soft web into the blood. The °flow stopped almost at once.

The rifle was on the ground. Pepé picked it up, °levered a new shell into the chamber. And then he slid into the brush on his stomach. Far to the right he crawled, and then up the hill, moving slowly and carefully, crawling to cover and resting and then crawling again.

In the mountains the sun is high in its °arc before it °penetrates the °gorges. The hot face looked over the hill and brought instant heat with it. The white light °beat on the rocks and °reflected from them and rose up quivering from the earth again, and the rocks and bushes seemed to quiver behind the air.

Pepé crawled in the general direction of the ridge peak, °zig-zagging for cover. The deep cut between his knuckles began to °throb. He crawled close to a rattlesnake before he saw it, and when it raised its dry head and made a soft beginning °whirr, he °backed up and took another way. The quick grey lizards flashed in front of him, raising a °tiny line of dust. He found another mass of spider web and pressed it against his throbbing hand.

Pepé was pushing the rifle with his left hand now. Little °drops of sweat ran to the ends of his coarse black hair and rolled down his cheeks. His lips and tongue were growing thick and heavy. His lips °writhed to draw °saliva

gather ['gæðə] *sammeln*

spider web ['spaidə web] *Spinn(en)gewebe*
cut [kʌt] *Schnittverletzung*
plaster into the blood ['plɑːstə] *hier: wie ein Pflaster auf die blutende Stelle drücken*
flow [fləu] *Fließen, hier: Blutstrom*
lever a new shell into the chamber ['liːvə] *hier: durchladen*

arc [ɑːk] *Bogen*
penitrate ['penitreit] *durchdringen, eindringen in*
gorge [gɔːdʒ] *enge (Fels-) Schlucht*
beat [biːt] *hier: brennen*
reflect [ri'flekt] *zurückstrahlen*

zig-zag ['zigzæg] *sich zickzackförmig od. im Zickzack bewegen*
throb [θrɔb] *pochen, hämmern*

whirr [wəː] *hier: Zischen*
back up *sich rückwärts bewegen, hier: rückwärts kriechen*
tiny ['taini] *winzig*

drop of sweat [swet] *Schweißtropfen*

writhe [raið] *sich krümmen od. verzerren*
saliva [sə'laivə] *Speichel*

35

into his mouth. His little dark eyes were °uneasy and suspicious. Once when a grey lizard paused in front of him on the parched ground and turned its head sideways he °crushed it flat with a stone.

When the sun °slid past noon he had not gone a mile. He crawled °exhaustedly a last hundred yards to a °patch of high sharp manzanita, crawled °desperately, and when the patch was reached he wriggled in among the tough °gnarly trunks and dropped his head on his left arm. There was little shade in the °meager brush, but there was cover and safety. Pepé went to sleep as he lay and the sun beat on his back. A few little birds °hopped close to him and °peered and hopped away. Pepé °squirmed in his sleep and he raised and dropped his wounded hand again and again.

The sun went down behind the peaks and the cool evening came, and then the dark. A coyote °yelled from the hillside, Pepé °started awake and looked about with °misty eyes. His hand was swollen and heavy; °a little thread of pain ran up the inside of his arm and °settled in a °pocket in his °armpit. He peered about and then stood up, for the mountains were black and the moon had not yet risen. Pepé stood up in the dark. The coat of his father pressed on his arm. His tongue was swollen until it nearly filled his mouth. He wriggled out of the coat and dropped it in the brush, and then he struggled up the hill, falling over rocks and °tearing his way through the brush.

uneasy [ʌn'iːzi] *unruhig, nervös*

crush [krʌʃ] *zermalmen, zerquetschen*

slid past noon [pɑːst, nuːn] *von* slide past noon *den Höhepunkt überschreiten*
exhausted [igˈzɔːstid] *erschöpft*
patch [pætʃ] *Fleck, Stelle*
desperate [ˈdespərit] *verzweifelt*

gnarly [ˈnɑːli] *knorrig*

meager AE [ˈmiːgə] *spärlich*

hop [hɔp] *hüpfen*

peer [piə] *spähen, schauen, starren*
squirm [skwəːm] *sich krümmen od. winden*

yell [jel] *gellend schreien*

start awake *hier: mit e-m Ruck aufwachen*
misty *verschleiert*
a little thread of pain [θred] *ein dünner schmerzender Strich*
settle *hier: sich festsetzen*
pocket [ˈpɔkit] *hier: Nest*
armpit [ˈɑːmpit] *Achselhöhle*

tear one's way through [teə, θruː] *hier: sich e-n Weg bahnen durch*

The rifle °knocked against stones as he went. Little °dry avalanches of °gravel and °shattered stone went whispering down the hill behind him.

After a while the old moon came up and showed the jagged ridge top ahead of him. By moonlight Pepé °traveled more easily. He bent forward so that his throbbing arm hung away from his body. The journey °uphill was made in °dashes and °rests, a frantic °rush up a few yards and then a rest. The wind coasted down the slope °rattling the dry stems of the bushes.

The moon was °at meridian when Pepé came at last to the sharp °backbone of the ridge top. On the last hundred yards of the °rise no °soil had °clung under the °wearing winds. The way was on °solid rock. He °clambered to the top and looked down on the other side. There was a °draw like the last below him, misty with moonlight, °brushed with dry °struggling sage and chaparral. On the other side the hill rose up sharply and at the top the jagged rotten teeth of the mountain °showed against the sky. At the bottom of the °cut the brush was thick and dark.

Pepé stumbled down the hill. His °throat was almost closed °with thirst. At first he tried to run, but °immediately he fell and rolled. After that he went more carefully. The moon was just disappearing behind the mountains when he came to the bottom. He crawled into the heavy brush feeling with his fingers for water. There was no water in the bed of the stream, only

knock [nɔk] schlagen, stoßen

dry avalanche ['ævəlɑːnʃ] Staublawine
gravel ['grævəl] Kies, Geröll
shattered ['ʃætəd] zersplittert, geborsten

travel ['trævl], traveled AE = travelled BE hier: sich fortbewegen

uphill ['ʌp'hil] bergauf, den Berg hinauf
dash [dæʃ] Vorstoß, schneller Anlauf
rest Ruhepause
rush [rʌʃ] Vorwärtsstürmen
rattle rütteln (an)
at meridian [mə'ridiən] auf dem höchsten Punkt
backbone ['bækbəun] Rücken, Hauptgebirgszug

rise [raiz] Aufstieg; Steigung
soil [sɔil] Erde, Erdreich
clung [klʌŋ] von cling [kliŋ] hier: sich halten können
wearing winds ['wɛəriŋ] hier: zerstörerische Kräfte des Windes
solid ['sɔlid] fest, hart
clamber ['klæmbə] (mühsam) klettern
draw AE [drɔː] kleines schmales Tal
brushed AE [brʌʃt] bedeckt, bewachsen
struggling ['strʌgliŋ] hier: kümmerlich
show against [ʃəu] hier: sich abzeichnen gegen
cut Einschnitt, Graben

throat [θrəut] Kehle
with thirst [θəːst] vor Durst
immediately [i'miːdjətli] sofort

damp earth. Pepé laid his gun down and °scooped up a handful of °mud and put it in his mouth, and then he °spluttered and °scraped the earth from his tongue with his finger, for the mud °drew at his mouth like a °poultice. He dug a hole in the stream bed with his fingers, dug a little basin to catch water; but before it was very deep his head fell forward on the damp ground and he slept.

The dawn came and the heat of the day fell on the earth, and still Pepé slept. Late in the afternoon his head °jerked up. He looked slowly around. His eyes were °slits of °wariness. Twenty feet away in the heavy brush a big °tawny °mountain lion stood looking at him. Its long thick tail °waved °gracefully, its ears were °erect with interest, not laid back dangerously. The lion °squatted down on its stomach and watched him.

Pepé looked at the hole he had dug in the earth. A half inch of °muddy water had °collected in the bottom. He °tore the sleeve from his °hurt arm, with his teeth °ripped out a little square, °soaked it in the water and put it in his mouth. °Over and over he filled the cloth and °sucked it.

Still the lion sat and watched him. The evening came down but there was no movement on the hills. No birds visited the dry bottom of the cut. Pepé looked °occasionally at the lion. The eyes of the yellow °beast °drooped as though he were about to sleep. He yawned and his long thin red tongue °curled out. Suddenly his head jerked

scoop up [sku:p] *(auf)schaufeln*
mud [mʌd] *Schlamm*
splutter ['splʌtə] *spucken*
scrape [skreip] *kratzen, schaben*
drew at [dru:] *von* draw at *hier: zusammenziehen, ziehen an*
poultice ['pəultis] *Breipackung, -umschlag*

jerk up *hochschnellen*

wariness ['weərinis] *Vorsicht, Wachsamkeit*
slits of wariness *wachsame Schlitze*
tawny ['tɔ:ni] *gelbbraun, lohfarben*
mountain lion ['laiən] *Puma*
wave [weiv] *hier: sich bewegen*
graceful ['greisful] *anmutig*
erect [i'rekt] *aufgerichtet, aufrecht*
squat down [skwɔt] *sich hinhocken, hier: sich hinlegen*
muddy ['mʌdi] *schlammig*
collect [kə'lekt] *sich (an)sammeln*
tore [tɔ:] *von* tear *abreißen*
hurt [hə:t] *verletzt, verwundet*
rip out *herausreißen*
soak [səuk] *durchtränken*
over and over = over and over again ['əuvə] *immer wieder*
suck [sʌk] *saugen an, aussaugen*

occasionally [ə'keiʒnəli] *gelegentlich, hin u. wieder*
beast [bi:st] *Tier*
droop [dru:p] *(schlaff) herabsinken od. herabhängen, hier: sich senken*
curl out [kə:l] *herausrollen*

38

around and his nostrils quivered. His big tail °lashed. He stood up and °slunk like a tawny shadow into the thick brush.

A moment later Pepé heard the sound, the °faint far crash of horses' hooves on gravel. And he heard something else, a high °whining °yelp of a dog.

Pepé took his rifle in his left hand and he glided into the brush almost as quietly as the lion had. In the darkening evening he °crouched up the hill toward the next ridge. Only when the dark came did he stand up. His energy was short. Once it was dark he fell over the rocks and slipped to his knees on the steep slope, but he moved on and on up the hill, °climbing and °scrabbling over the °broken hillside.

When he was far up toward the top, he lay down and slept for a little while. The °withered moon, shining on his face, awakened him. He stood up and moved up the hill. Fifty yards away he stopped and turned back, for he had forgotten his rifle. He walked heavily down and °poked about in the brush, but he could not find his gun. At last he lay down to rest. The pocket of pain in his armpit had grown more sharp. His arm seemed to °swell out and °fall with every heartbeat. There was no °position lying down where the heavy arm did not press against his armpit.

With the °effort of a hurt beast, Pepé got up and moved again toward the top of the ridge. He held his swollen arm away from his body with his left hand. Up the steep hill he °dragged

lash [læʃ] *peitschen, schlagen*
slunk [slʌŋk] *von* slink [sliŋk] *schleichen*

faint [feint] *schwach*

whining *winselnd, wimmernd*
yelp [jelp] *Gekläff*

crouch up the hill [krautʃ] *geduckt den Abhang hinauflaufen*

climb [klaim] *klettern*
scrabble [ˈskræbl] *krabbeln*
broken hillside *unebener (Ab-)Hang*

withered *hier: abnehmend*

poke about [pəuk] *(herum-)suchen*

swell out *anschwellen*
fall [fɔːl] *hier: in sich zusammensinken*
position [pəˈziʃən] *Stellung, Lage*

effort [ˈefət] *Anstrengung, hier: letzte Kraft*

drag o.s. [dræg] *sich schleppen*

himself, a few steps and a rest, and a few more steps. At last he was nearing the top. The moon showed the uneven sharp back of it against the sky.

Pepé's °brain °spun in a big °spiral up and away from him. He °slumped to the ground and lay still. The rock ridge top was only a hundred feet above him.

The moon moved over the sky. Pepé half turned on his back. His tongue tried to make words, but only a °thick °hissing came from between his lips.

When the dawn came, Pepé pulled himself up. His eyes were °sane again. He drew his great °puffed arm in front of him and looked at the °angry °wound. The black line ran up from his wrist to his armpit. Automatically he °reached in his pocket for the big black knife, but it was not there. His eyes °searched the ground. He picked up a sharp °blade of stone and scraped at the wound, °sawed at the °proud flesh and then °squeezed the green juice out in big drops. Instantly he threw back his head and whined like a dog. His whole right side °shuddered at the pain, but the pain cleared his head.

In the grey light he struggled up the last slope to the ridge and crawled over and lay down behind a line of rocks. Below him lay a deep canyon exactly like the last, waterless and desolate. There was no flat, no oak trees, not even heavy brush in the bottom of it. And on the other side a sharp ridge stood up, thinly brushed with

brain [brein] *Gehirn*
spun [spʌn] *von* spin *sich drehen, wirbeln*
spiral ['spaiərəl] *Spirale*
slump to the ground [slʌmp, graund] *zu Boden sinken*

thick [θik] *dumpf, belegt, heiser*
hissing ['hisiŋ] *Zischen*

sane [sein] *normal*
puffed [pʌft] *(an)geschwollen*
angry ['æŋgri] *entzündet, schlimm*
wound [wuːnd] *Wunde*

reach [riːtʃ] *greifen, langen*

search [səːtʃ] *absuchen*
blade of stone *klingenähnlicher Stein*
saw [sɔː] *sägen*
proud flesh [praud fleʃ] *wildes Fleisch*
squeeze out *herauspressen*

shudder at ['ʃʌdə] *zittern bei*

starving sage, °littered with broken granite. Strewn over the hill there were giant outcroppings, and on the top the granite teeth stood out against the sky.

littered ['litəd] *übersät, dicht bedeckt*

The new day was light now. The flame of the sun came over the ridge and fell on Pepé where he lay on the ground. His coarse black hair was littered with twigs and bits of spider web. His eyes had °retreated back into his head. Between his lips the tip of his black tongue showed.

retreat back [ri'tri:t] *sich zurückziehen, zurückweichen, hier: tief einsinken*

He sat up and °dragged his great arm into his lap and °nursed it, °rocking his body and moaning in his throat. He threw back his head and looked up into the pale sky. A big black bird °circled nearly out of sight, and far to the left another was sailing near.

drag *zerren, ziehen*
nurse [nə:s] *schützend umfassen*
rock [rɔk] *wiegen, schaukeln*

circle ['sə:kl] *kreisen*

He lifted his head to listen, for a familiar sound had come to him from the valley he had climbed out of; it was the crying yelp of °hounds, excited and °feverish, on a trail.

hound [haund] *Jagdhund*
feverish ['fi:vəriʃ] *aufgeregt, fieberhaft*

Pepé °bowed his head quickly. He tried to speak rapid words but only a thick °hiss came from his lips. He °drew a °shaky cross on his breast with his left hand. It was a long °struggle to get to his feet. He crawled slowly and °mechanically to the top of a big rock on the ridge peak. Once there, he arose slowly, °swaying to his feet, and stood erect. Far below he could see the dark brush where he had slept. He °braced his feet and stood there, black against the morning sky.

bow one's head [bau, hed] *den Kopf neigen od. senken*
hiss [his] *Zischen*
drew a cross [dru:, krɔs] *von draw a cross ein Kreuz schlagen*
shaky ['ʃeiki] *zitt(e)rig*
struggle *Anstrengung, Kampf*
mechanical [mi'kænikəl] *mechanisch*
sway [swei] *schwanken*

brace AE [breis] *hier: in den Boden stemmen*

There came a °ripping sound at his feet. A piece of stone flew up and a bul-

ripping ['ripiŋ] *hier: splitternd*

let °droned off into the next gorge. The °hollow crash echoed up from below. Pepé looked down for a moment and then °pulled himself straight again.

His body °jarred back. His left hand °fluttered helplessly toward his breast. The second crash sounded from below. Pepé swung forward and °toppled from the rock. His body °struck and rolled over and over, starting a little avalanche. And when at last he stopped against a bush, the avalanche slid slowly down and °covered up his head.

drone off [drəun] *hier: surrend davon-* od. *weiterfliegen*
hollow ['hɔləu] *dumpf, hohl*

pull o.s. straight [streit] *sich gerade aufrichten*
jar back [dʒɑ:] *zurücktaumeln*
flutter ['flʌtə] *flattern*

topple ['tɔpl] *stürzen, kippen*
struck [strʌk] *von* strike [straik] *aufschlagen*

cover up (*ganz*) *zudecken*

# The °Harness

Peter Randall was one of the most highly respected farmers of °Monterey °County. Once, before he was to °make a little speech at a °Masonic °convention, the brother who introduced him °referred to him as an example for young °Masons of California to °emulate. He was °nearing fifty; his °manner was grave and °restrained, and he wore a carefully °tended beard. From every °gathering he °reaped the °authority that belongs to the bearded man. Peter's eyes were grave, too; blue and grave almost °to the point of °sorrowfulness. People knew there was °force in him, but force held °caged. Sometimes, for no °apparent reason, his eyes °grew °sullen and °mean, like the eyes of a bad dog; but that look soon °passed, and the °restraint and °probity came back into his face. He was tall and broad. He held his shoulders back as though they were °braced, and he °sucked in his stomach like a soldier. °Inasmuch as farmers are usually °slouchy men, Peter °gained an °added respect because of his °posture.

°Concerning Peter's wife, Emma, people generally agreed that it was hard to see how such a little °skin-and-bones woman could go on living, °particularly when she was sick most of the time. She weighed eighty-

harness ['hɑːnis] *hier: Korsett*
Monterey [mɔntəˈrei] *Stadt u. Halbinsel südöstl. von San Franzisko, Kalifornien.*
county AE ['kaunti] *(Verwaltungs)Bezirk, Kreis*
make a speech [meik, spiːtʃ] *e-e Rede halten*
Masonic [məˈsɔnik] *Freimaurer...*
convention [kənˈvenʃən] *Versammlung, Tagung*
refer to [riˈfəː] *verweisen auf*
Mason ['meisn] *Freimaurer*
emulate ['emjuleit] *nacheifern*
near [niə] *sich nähern*
manner ['mænə] *Auftreten*
restrained [riˈstreind] *zurückhaltend, beherrscht*
tended ['tendid] *gepflegt*
gathering ['gæðəriŋ] *Versammlung, Zusammenkunft*
reap [riːp] *ernten*
authority [ɔːˈθɔriti] *Autorität*
to the point of [pɔint] *bis an die Grenze zu ...*
sorrowfulness ['sɔrəfulnis] *Traurigkeit*
force [fɔːs] *Kraft, Stärke*
caged [keidʒd] *hier: gebändigt*
apparent [əˈpærənt] *ersichtlich*
grew [gruː] *von* grow [grəu] *werden*
sullen ['sʌlən] *mürrisch*
mean AE [miːn] *bösartig*
pass [pɑːs] *vorübergehen*
restraint [riˈstreint] *Beherrschtheit, Zurückhaltung*
probity ['prəubiti] *Redlichkeit*
braced [breist] *versteift*
suck in [sʌk] *hier: einziehen*
inasmuch as [inəzˈmʌtʃ] *da*
slouchy ['slautʃi] *krumm, mit krummer Haltung*
gain [gəin] *sich verschaffen*

seven pounds. At forty-five, her face was as wrinkled and brown as that of an old, old woman, but her dark eyes were °feverish with a °determination to live. She was a proud woman, who complained very little. Her father had been a thirty-third °degree Mason and °Worshipful Master of the °Grand Lodge of California. Before he died he had taken °a great deal of interest in Peter's Masonic °career.

Once a year Peter went away for a week, leaving his wife alone on the farm. To neighbors who called to °keep her company she °invariably explained, °"He's away on a business trip."

Each time Peter returned from a business trip, Emma was °ailing for a month or two, and this was °hard on Peter, for Emma did her own work and refused to °hire a girl. When she was ill, Peter had to do the housework.

The Randall °ranch lay across the °Salinas River, next to the °foothills. It was an ideal balance of °bottom and °upland. Forty-five acres of °rich °level °soil brought from the °cream of the county by the river in old times and spread out as °flat as a board; and eighty acres of °gentle upland for hay and °orchard. The white farmhouse was as °neat and restrained as its owners. The °immediate °yard was °fenced, and in the garden, under Emma's °direction, Peter °raised °button dahlias and °immortelles, °carnations and °pinks.

From the front °porch one could look down over the °flat to the river

added ['ædid] *zusätzlich*
posture ['pɔstʃə] *Haltung*
concerning [kən'sɜːniŋ] *was betraf od. anbelangte*
skin-and-bones ['skinən'bəunz] *aus Haut u. Knochen bestehend*
particularly [pə'tikjuləli] *besonders*

be feverish with ['fiːvəriʃ] *hier: glänzen vor*
determination [ditəːmiˈneiʃən] *Entschlossenheit*
degree [diˈgriː] *Grad*
Worshipful Master ['wɜːʃipful 'maːstə] *Großmeister*
Grand Lodge [grænd lɔdʒ] *Großloge*
a great deal of [greit diːl] *sehr viel*
career [kəˈriə] *Karriere*
keep s.o. company [kiːp 'kʌmpəni] *j-m Gesellschaft leisten*
invariably [in'vɛəriəbli] *stets*
be away on a business trip ['biznis trip] *auf e-r Geschäftsreise sein*
ailing ['eiliŋ] *leidend, kränklich*
be hard on s.o. [haːd] *hart für j-n sein*
hire s.o. ['haiə] *j-n einstellen*
ranch [raːntʃ, AE ræntʃ] *Ranch, Viehfarm, hier: Farm*
Salinas [səˈliːnəs] *Fluß u. Stadt*
foothills *Pl* ['futhilz] *Ausläufer Pl e-s (hier: des) Gebirges*
bottom ['bɔtəm] *Schwemmland*
upland ['ʌplənd] *Hochland*
rich [ritʃ] *fett, fruchtbar*
level ['levl] *eben*
soil [sɔil] *Erde, Erdreich*
cream [kriːm] *hier: (das) Beste*
flat [flæt] *flach*
gentle ['dʒentl] *hier: sanft ansteigend*
orchard ['ɔːtʃəd] *Obstgarten*
neat [niːt] *sauber, gepflegt*
immediate [iˈmiːdjət] *unmittelbar angrenzend*
yard [jaːd] *Hof(raum)*
fenced [fenst] *eingezäunt*
direction [diˈrekʃən] *Anleitung*
raise [reiz] *ziehen, anbauen*

°with its sheath of °willows and °cottonwoods, and across the river to the °beet fields, and past the fields to the °bulbous °dome of the Salinas °courthouse. Often in the afternoon Emma sat in a °rocking chair on the front porch, until the °breeze drove her in. She °knitted °constantly, looking up now and then to watch Peter working on the flat or in the orchard, or on the °slope below the house.

The Randall ranch was no more °encumbered with °mortgage than any of the others in the valley. The °crops, °judiciously chosen and carefully °tended, paid the °interest, °made a °reasonable living and left a few hundred dollars every year °toward °paying off the °principal. It was no wonder that Peter Randall was respected by his neighbors, and that his seldom spoken words were given attention even when they were about the weather or the way things were going. Let Peter say, "I'm going to kill a pig Saturday," and nearly every one of his hearers went home and killed a pig on Saturday. They didn't know why, but if Peter Randall was going to kill a pig, it seemed like a good, safe, °conservative thing to do.

Peter and Emma were married for twenty-one years. They collected a houseful of good furniture, a number of °framed pictures, vases of all shapes, and books of a °sturdy type. Emma had no children. The house was °unscarred, °uncarved, °unchalked. On the front and back porches °footscrapers and thick °cocoa-fiber °mats kept °dirt out of the house.

button dahlia ['bʌtn 'deiljə] Ball-, Pompondahlie
immortelle [imɔ:'tel] Immortelle, Strohblume
carnation [kɑ:'neiʃən] Gartennelke
pink [piŋk] (Feder)Nelke
porch AE [pɔ:tʃ] Veranda
flat Niederung; ebenes Feld

with its sheath of [ʃi:θ] hier: gesäumt von
willow ['wiləu] Weide
cottonwood ['kɔtnwud] (amerikanische) Pappel
beet [bi:t] Rübe
bulbous ['bʌlbəs] knollenförmig
dome [dəum] Kuppel(dach)
courthouse AE ['kɔ:thaus] Verwaltungs- u. Gerichtsgebäude
rocking chair ['rɔkiŋ tʃɛə] Schaukelstuhl
breeze [bri:z] Brise
knit [nit] stricken
constant ['kɔnstənt] ständig
slope [sləup] (Ab)Hang
encumbered [in'kʌmbəd] belastet
mortgage ['mɔ:gidʒ] Hypothek
crop [krɔp] hier: (Aus)Saat
judicious [dʒu:'diʃəs] klug, wohlüberlegt, hier: sorgfältig
tended ['tendid] gehütet
interest ['intrist] Zins(en Pl)
made a ... living [meid, 'livin] von make a ... living [meik] hier: für e-n ... Lebensunterhalt sorgen
reasonable ['ri:znəbl] angemessen
toward [tə'wɔ:d] (als Beitrag) zu
pay off [pei] abzahlen
principal ['prinsəpəl] hier: Schulden Pl
conservative [kən'sə:vətiv] hier: allgemein üblich
framed [freimd] gerahmt
sturdy ['stə:di] handfest, solide
unscarred [ʌn'skɑ:d] ohne Narben
was uncarved [ʌn'kɑ:vd] nichts war hineingeschnitzt

In the °intervals between her illnesses, Emma °saw to it that the house °was kept up. The °hinges of doors and °cupboards were °oiled, and no °screws were °gone from the °catches. The furniture and °woodwork were freshly °varnished once a year. °Repairs were usually made after Peter came home from his yearly business trips.

Whenever the word went around among the farms that Emma was sick again, the neighbors °waylaid the doctor as he drove by on the river road.

"Oh, I °guess she'll be all right," he answered their questions. °"She'll have to °stay in bed for °a couple of weeks."

The good neighbors took cakes to the Randall farm, and they °tiptoed into the °sickroom, where the little °skinny bird of a woman lay in a °tremendous °walnut bed. She looked at them with her °bright little dark eyes.

"Wouldn't you like the curtains up a little, °dear?" they asked.

"No, thank you. The light °worries my eyes."

"Is there anything we can do for you?"

"No, thank you. Peter °does for me very well."

"Just remember, if there's anything you think of—"

Emma was such a °tight woman. There was nothing you could do for her when she was ill, except to take °pies and cakes to Peter. Peter °would be in the kitchen, wearing a neat,

unchalked [ʌnˈtʃɔːkt] *nicht mit Kreide beschmiert*
footscraper [ˈfutskreipə] *Fußabstreifer*
coco(a)-fiber AE [ˈkəukəufaibə] *aus Kokosfasern*
mat [mæt] *Matte*
dirt [dəːt] *Schmutz*

interval [ˈintəvəl] *Zwischenzeit, hier: Pause, Zeit*
saw to it that [sɔː] *von see to it that* [siː] *dafür sorgen, daß*
was kept up [kept] *von keep up* [kiːp] *in Gang halten, hier: instand halten*
hinge [hindʒ] *(Tür)Angel*
cupboard [ˈkʌbəd] *Schrank*
oil [ɔil] *ölen*
screw [skruː] *Schraube*
be gone from [gɔn] *hier: fehlen an*
catch [kætʃ] *Klinke; (Tür-) Schloß*
woodwork [ˈwudwəːk] *Holzarbeiten Pl,-werk*
varnish [ˈvɑːniʃ] *lackieren, firnissen; (auf)polieren*
repairs Pl [riˈpɛəz] *Reparaturen*
waylaid [weiˈleid] *von waylay* [weiˈlei] *abfangen, auflauern*
guess AE [ges] *glauben, denken, meinen*
she'll have to [ʃiːl] = she will have to *sie muß*
stay [stei] *bleiben*
a couple of F [ˈkʌpl] *ein paar*
tiptoe [ˈtiptəu] *auf den Zehenspitzen gehen*
sickroom [ˈsikrum] *Krankenzimmer*
skinny [ˈskini] *mager, dürr*
tremendous [triˈmendəs] *riesig*
walnut [ˈwɔːlnʌt] *Walnuß; hier: aus Nußbaum*
bright [brait] *glänzend*
dear [diə] *meine Liebe (Anrede)*
worry [ˈwʌri] *hier: weh tun*
do for s.o. *hier: sorgen für*
tight [tait] *hier: verschlossen*

pie [pai] *Pastete*
would [wud] *pflegte zu (oft unübersetzt)*

clean apron. He would be filling a °hot-water bottle or making °junket.

And so, one °fall, when the °news °traveled that Emma was °down, the farm-wives baked for Peter and °prepared to make their usual visits.

Mrs. Chappell, the next farm neighbor, stood on the river road when the doctor drove by. °"How's Emma Randall, doctor?"

"I don't think she's so very well, Mrs. Chappell. I think she's a °pretty sick woman."

Because to Dr. Marn anyone who wasn't actually a °corpse was °well on the road to recovery, the word went about among the farms that Emma Randall was going to die.

It was a long, terrible illness. Peter himself gave °enemas and carried °bedpans. The doctor's °suggestion that a °nurse be °employed met only °beady, °fierce °refusal in the eyes of the patient; and, ill as she was, her °demands were respected. Peter fed her and bathed her, and °made up the great walnut bed. The bedroom °curtains remained drawn.

It was two months before the dark, sharp bird eyes °veiled, and the sharp °mind °retired into °unconsciousness. And only then did a nurse come to the house. Peter was °lean and sick himself, not far from °collapse. The neighbors brought him cakes and pies, and found them uneaten in the kitchen when they called again.

Mrs. Chappell was in the house with Peter the afternoon Emma died. Peter became °hysterical °immediately.

hot-water bottle [hɔt'wɔːtə-bɔtl] *Wärmflasche*
junket ['dʒʌŋkit] *Quarkspeise (mit Sahne)*
fall AE [fɔːl] *Herbst*
news *Pl* [njuːz] *Neuigkeit, Nachricht*
travel ['trævl], traveled AE = travelled BE *hier: sich verbreiten*
down [daun] *bettlägerig*
prepare [pri'pɛə] *sich anschicken*
how's [hauz] = how is *wie geht es*
pretty ['priti] *ziemlich, recht*
corpse [kɔːps] *Leiche, Leichnam*
well on the road to recovery [rəud, ri'kʌvəri] *auf dem bestenWege der Besserung od. Genesung*
enema ['enimə] *Klistier, Einlauf*
bedpan ['bedpæn] *Bettschüssel*
suggestion [sə'dʒestʃən] *Vorschlag*
nurse [nəːs] *Krankenschwester, -pflegerin*
employ [im'plɔi] *einstellen*
beady ['biːdi] *rund u. glänzend (Augen)*
fierce [fiəs] *grimmig, wild, wütend, heftig*
refusal [ri'fjuːzəl] *Ablehnung*
demand [di'maːnd] *Forderung*
made up *von* make up *herrichten, (zurecht)machen*
curtains ... drawn ['kəːtnz, drɔːn] *von* draw the curtains [drɔː] *die Vorhänge zuziehen*
veil [veil] *sich verschleiern*
mind [maind] *Verstand*
retire [ri'taiə] *sich zurückziehen; abtreten; hier: hinübergleiten*
unconsciousness [ʌn'kɔnʃəsnis] *Bewußtlosigkeit*
lean [liːn] *mager*
collapse [kə'læps] *Kollaps, Zusammenbruch*

hysterical [his'terikəl] *hysterisch*
immediately [i'miːdjətli] *sofort*

47

Mrs. Chappell telephoned the doctor, and then she called her husband to come and help her, for Peter was °wailing like a crazy man, and beating his bearded cheeks with his fists. Ed Chappell was °ashamed when he saw him.

wail [weil] *jammern, schreien, heulen*

be ashamed [ə'ʃeimd] *sich schämen*

Peter's beard was wet with his tears. His loud °sobbing could be heard throughout the house. Sometimes he sat by the bed and covered his head with a pillow, and sometimes he °paced the floor of the bedroom °bellowing like a calf. When Ed Chappell °self-consciously put a hand on his shoulder and said, °"Come on, Peter, come on, now," in a helpless voice, Peter shook his hand off. The doctor drove out and signed the °certificate.

sobbing ['sɔbiŋ] *Schluchzen*

pace the floor [peis, flɔ:] *im Zimmer auf u. ab gehen*
bellow ['belou] *brüllen*

self-conscious ['self'kɔnʃəs] *befangen, unsicher*
come on *na, na!, komm, komm!*

When the °undertaker came, they °had a devil of a time with Peter. He was half mad. He fought them when they tried to take the °body away. It was only after Ed Chappell and the undertaker held him down while the doctor °stuck him with a °hypodermic, that they were able to remove Emma.

certificate = death certificate [deθ sə'tifikit] *Totenschein, Sterbeurkunde*
undertaker ['ʌndəteikə] *Leichenbestatter*
have a devil of a time F ['devl, taim] *es verdammt schwer haben*
body ['bɔdi] *Leiche*

The °morphine didn't put Peter to sleep. He sat °hunched in the corner, breathing heavily and staring at the floor.

stuck him with ... [stʌk] *von* stick him with ... *hier: ... verabreichen od. geben*
hypodermic [haipə'də:mik] *Spritze*
morphine ['mɔ:fi:n] *Morphium*
hunched [hʌntʃt] *zusammengekrümmt*

"Who's going to °stay with him?" the doctor asked. "Miss Jack?" to the nurse.

stay with s.o. *bei j-m bleiben*

"I couldn't °handle him, doctor, not alone."

"Will you stay, Chappell?"

°"Sure, I'll stay."

"Well, look. Here are some °triple °bromides. If he °gets going again, give

handle s.o. ['hændl] *mit j-m fertigwerden*
sure AE [ʃuə] *klar!, aber sicher!*
triple ['tripl] *dreifach, hier: sehr stark*
bromide ['brəumaid] *Bromid, hier: Beruhigungsmittel, -pille*
get going ['gəuiŋ] *hier: anfangen*

him one of these. And if they don't °work, here's some °sodium °amytal. One of these °capsules will °calm him down."

Before they went away, they helped the °stupefied Peter into the sitting-room and laid him gently down on a °sofa. Ed Chappell sat in an °easy chair and watched him. The bromides and a glass of water were on the table beside him.

The little sitting-room was clean and °dusted. Only that morning Peter had °swept the floor with pieces of damp newspaper. Ed °built a little fire in the °grate, and put on a couple of °pieces of °oak when the flames were well started. The dark had come early. A light rain °spattered against the windows when the wind drove it. Ed °trimmed the °kerosene lamps and °turned the flames low. In the grate the °blaze °snapped and °crackled and the flames °curled like hair over the oak. For a long time Ed sat in his easy chair watching Peter where he lay °drugged on the couch. At last Ed °dozed off to sleep.

It was about ten o'clock when he awakened. He °started up and looked toward the sofa. Peter was sitting up, looking at him. Ed's hand went out toward the bromide bottle, but Peter shook his head.

"No need to give me anything, Ed. I °guess the doctor °slugged me pretty hard, didn't he? I feel all right now, only a little °dopey."

work [wəːk] *hier: wirken*
sodium ['səudjəm] *Natrium*
amytal ['æmitæl] *ein schmerz-stillendes Mittel*
capsule ['kæpsjuːl] *Kapsel*
calm down [kɑːm] *beruhigen*
stupefied ['stjuːpifaid] *be-täubt*

sofa ['səufə] *Sofa*
easy chair ['iːzi tʃɛə] *Lehnstuhl, Sessel*

dusted ['dʌstid] *staubgewischt*
swept [swept] *von* sweep [swiːp] *kehren, fegen*
built a fire [bilt, 'faiə] *von* build a fire [bild] *(ein) Feuer machen*
grate [greit] *(Feuer)Rost, Ka-min*
piece [piːs] *hier: Scheit*
oak [əuk] *Eichenholz*
spatter ['spætə] *spritzen*
trim a lamp *e-e Lampe putzen (Docht verschneiden)*
kerosene ['kerəsiːn] *Kerosin, Petroleum*
turn low [təːn ləu] *klein(er) drehen, herunterschrauben*
blaze [bleiz] *loderndes Feuer, (lodernde) Flamme*
snap [snæp] *krachen*
crackle ['krækl] *knistern, pras-seln*
curl [kəːl] *hier: sich ringeln*
drugged [drʌgd] *betäubt*
doze off [dəuz] *einnicken, -duseln*
start up [stɑːt] *auffahren, hochschrecken*

guess AE *annehmen, vermuten, glauben*
slug AE [slʌg] *hart schlagen, hier: F e-e (hier: = Spritze) verpassen*
dopey ['dəupi] *benommen, be-nebelt*

49

"If you'll just take one of these, you'll get some sleep."

"I don't want sleep." He °fingered his °draggled beard and then stood up. "I'll go out and wash my face, then I'll feel better."

Ed heard him °running water in the kitchen. In a moment he came back into the living-room, still drying his face on a towel. Peter was smiling °curiously. It was an expression Ed had never seen on him before, a °quizzical, °wondering smile. "I guess °I kind of °broke loose when she died, didn't I?" Peter said.

"Well—yes, you °carried on °some."

"It seemed like something °snapped inside of me," Peter explained. "Something like a °suspender strap. It °made me all °come apart. I'm all right, now, though."

Ed looked down at the floor and saw a little brown °spider °crawling, and stretched out his foot and °stomped it.

Peter asked suddenly, "Do you believe in an °afterlife?"

Ed Chappell °squirmed. He didn't like to talk about such things, for to talk about them was to bring them up in his mind and think about them. "Well, yes. I °suppose if you °come right down to it, I do."

"Do you believe that somebody that's—°passed on—can look down and see what we're doing?"

"Oh, I don't know as I'd go that far —I don't know."

Peter went on as though he were talking to himself. "Even if she could see me, and I didn't do what she want-

finger ['fiŋgə] *betasten*

draggled ['drægld] *schmutzig, beschmutzt*

run [rʌn] *laufen lassen*

curious ['kjuəriəs] *seltsam, merkwürdig*

quizzical ['kwizikəl] *komisch, seltsam*

wondering ['wʌndəriŋ] *verwundert, erstaunt*

I kind of [kaind] *ich bin wohl etwas* od. *irgendwie*

broke loose [brəuk lu:s] *von* break loose [breik] *hier: zusammenbrechen*

carried on F ['kærid] *von* carry on ['kæri] *e-e Szene machen*

some AE F [sʌm] *ziemlich*

snap *zerreißen, -brechen*

suspender strap AE [səs'pendə stræp] *ein Träger e-s Hosenträgers*

made *von* make (*j-n*) *lassen*

come apart [kaind ə'pɑ:t] *auseinander-, zusammenbrechen*

spider ['spaidə] *Spinne*

crawl [krɔ:l] *kriechen*

stomp AE [stɔmp] *zertreten*

afterlife ['ɑ:ftəlaif] *Leben nach dem Tode*

squirm [skwə:m] *sich winden*

suppose [sə'pəuz] *glauben, meinen, denken*

come right down to it F *hier: es sich richtig überlegen*

pass on [pɑ:s] *sterben, verscheiden*

ed, she °ought to feel good because I did it when she was here. It ought to please her that she made a good man of me. If I wasn't a good man when she wasn't here, °that'd °prove she did it all, wouldn't it? I was a good man, wasn't I, Ed?"

"What do you mean, 'was'?"

"Well, °except for one week a year I was good. I don't know what I'll do now...." His face grew angry. °"Except one thing." He stood up and °stripped off his coat and his shirt. Over his °underwear there was a °web harness that pulled his shoulders back. He °unhooked the harness and threw it off. Then he °dropped his trousers, °disclosing a wide °elastic °belt. He °shucked this off over his feet, and then he °scratched his stomach °luxuriously before he °put on his clothes again. He smiled at Ed, the strange, wondering smile, again. "I don't know how she °got me to do things, but she did. She didn't seem to °boss me, but she always °made me do things. You know, I don't think I believe in an afterlife. When she was alive, even when she was sick, I had to do things she wanted, but just the minute she died, it was—why like that harness coming off! I couldn't °stand it. It was all over. I'm going to have to °get used to going without that harness." He shook his finger in Ed's direction. "My stomach's going to °stick out," he said °positively. "I'm going to let it stick out. Why, I'm fifty years old."

Ed didn't like that. He wanted to get away. This sort of thing wasn't

ought to [ɔːt] *sollte*

that'd ['ðætid] = that would
prove [pruːv] *beweisen*

except (for) [ik'sept] *bis auf, abgesehen von, außer*

strip off *ausziehen*

underwear ['ʌndəwɛə] *Unterwäsche*
web [web] *Stoff...*
unhook ['ʌn'huk] *aufhaken*
drop [drɔp] *fallen lassen*
disclose [dis'kləuz] *zeigen, enthüllen*
elastic [i'læstik] *elastisch*
belt [belt] *Gürtel, Gurt*
shuck off [ʃʌk] *hier: abstreifen*
scratch [skrætʃ] *kratzen*
luxurious [lʌg'zjuəriəs] *genüßlich, wohlig*
put on *anziehen*
got ..., made ... [gɔt, meid] *von* get *od.* make s.o. to do s.th. *j-n dazu bringen, et. zu tun*
boss [bɔs] *kommandieren*

stand [stænd] *ertragen, aushalten*

get used to [juːst] *sich gewöhnen an*

stick out *hervor-, herausstehen*
positive ['pɔzətiv] *bestimmt*

very °decent. "If you'll just take one of these, you'll get some sleep," he said weakly.

Peter had not put his coat on. He was sitting on the sofa in an open shirt. "I don't want to sleep. I want to talk. I guess I'll have to °put that belt and harness on for the °funeral, but after that I'm going to burn them. Listen, I've got a bottle of °whiskey in the °barn. °I'll go get it."

"Oh no," Ed °protested quickly. "I couldn't drink now, not at a time like this."

Peter stood up. "Well, I could. You can sit and watch me if you want. I tell you, it's all over." He went °out the door, leaving Ed Chappell unhappy and °scandalized. It was only a moment before he was back. He started talking as he came through the °doorway with the whiskey. "I only got one thing in my life, those °trips. Emma was a pretty °bright woman. She knew °I'd've gone crazy if I didn't get away once a year. God, how she °worked on my °conscience when I came back!" His voice °lowered °confidentially. "You know what I did on those trips?"

Ed's eyes were wide open now. Here was a man he didn't know, and he was becoming °fascinated. He took the glass of whiskey when it was °handed to him. "No, what did you do?"

Peter °gulped his drink and °coughed, and wiped his mouth with his hand. "I °got drunk," he said. "I went to °fancy houses in San Francisco. I was drunk for a week, and I went to a fancy house every night." He °poured his

be decent ['diːsnt] *schicklich sein, sich gehören*

put on *hier: umtun*

funeral ['fjuːnərəl] *Begräbnis, Beerdigung*

whiskey AE = whisky BE ['wiski] *Whisky*
barn [bɑːn] *Scheune*
I'll go get it = I shall *od.* will go and get it
protest [prə'test] *protestieren*

out AE = out of BE *zu ... hinaus*

scandalized ['skændəlaizd] *schockiert, entrüstet*

doorway ['dɔːwei] *Türöffnung*

trip *Ausflug, Spritztour; kurze Reise*
bright [brait] *klug, gescheit*
I'd've gone ['aidəv gɔn] = I would have gone *ich wäre geworden*
work on *bearbeiten*
conscience ['kɔnʃəns] *Gewissen*
lower ['ləuə] *sich senken*
confidential [kɔnfi'denʃəl] *vertraulich*

fascinated ['fæsineitid] *fasziniert*
hand s.th. to s.o. [hænd] *j-m et. reichen*
gulp [gʌlp] *hinunterschlucken, hier: hinunterstürzen*
cough [kɔf] *husten*
got drunk [drʌŋk] *von* get drunk *sich betrinken*
fancy house ['fænsi haus] *Bordell, Freudenhaus*

pour [pɔː] *gießen*

glass full again. "I guess Emma knew, but she never said anything. °I'd've *busted* if I hadn't got away."

Ed Chappell °sipped his whiskey °gingerly. "She always said you went on business."

Peter looked at his glass and drank it, and poured it full again. His eyes had begun to shine. "Drink your drink, Ed. I know you think it isn't right—so soon, but no one'll know but you and me. °Kick up the fire. I'm not sad."

Chappell went to the grate and °stirred the °glowing wood until °lots of °sparks flew up the chimney like little shining birds. Peter filled the glasses and °retired to the sofa again. When Ed went back to the chair he sipped from his glass and °pretended he didn't know it was °filled up. His cheeks were °flushing. It didn't seem so terrible, now, to be drinking. The afternoon and the death had °receded into an °indefinite °past.

°"Want some cake?" Peter asked. °"There's half a dozen cakes in the °pantry."

"No, °I don't think I will °thank you for some."

"You know," Peter °confessed, "I don't think I'll eat cake again. For ten years, every time Emma was sick, people sent cakes. It was nice of °'em, of course, only now cake means sickness to me. Drink your drink."

Something happened in the room. Both men looked up, trying to discover what it was. The room was somehow different than it had been a moment before. Then Peter smiled °sheepishly.

"It was °that °mantel clock stopped. I don't think I'll start it any more. I'll get a little quick °alarm clock that °ticks °fast. That °clack-clack-clack is too °mournful." He °swallowed his whiskey. "I guess you'll be telling around that I'm crazy, won't you?"

Ed looked up from his glass, and smiled and °nodded. "No, I will not. I can see pretty much how you feel about things. I didn't know you wore that harness and belt."

"A man ought to stand up °straight," Peter said. "'I'm a °natural sloucher." °Then he exploded: "I'm a natural fool! For twenty years I've been pretending I was a wise, good man—except for that one week a year." He said loudly, "Things have been °dribbled to me. My life's been °dribbled out to me. Here, let me fill your glass. I've got another bottle out in the barn, °way down under a °pile of °sacks."

Ed held out his glass to be filled. Peter went on, "I thought how it would be nice to have my whole river flat in °sweet peas. Think how °it'd be to sit on the front porch and see all those acres of blue and pink, °just solid. And when the wind came up over them, think of the big °smell. A big smell that would almost °knock you over."

"A lot of men have gone °broke on sweet peas. °'Course you get a big price for the °seed, but too many things can happen to your crop."

°"I don't give a damn," Peter shouted. "I want a lot of everything. I want forty acres of °color and smell. I want fat women, with °breasts as

mantel ['mæntl] *Abkzg für* mantelpiece, mantelshelf *Kaminsims, hier: auf dem Kaminsims*

... that mantel clock stopped [klɔk, stɔpt] = ... that mantel clock that stopped

alarm clock [ə'lɑːm] *Wecker*

tick *ticken*

fast [fɑːst] *schnell, flott*

clack [klæk] *Ticktack*

mournful ['mɔːnful] *düster, traurig*

swallow ['swɔləu] *hinunterschlucken, hier: hintergießen*

nod [nɔd] *nicken*

straight [streit] *gerade, aufrecht*

natural ['nætʃrəl] *geboren, von Natur aus*

I am a natural sloucher ['slautʃə] *von Natur aus habe ich e-e sehr schlechte Haltung*

then he exploded [iks'pləudid] *dann brach es aus ihm hervor*

dribble (out) ['dribl] *in kleinen Mengen od. Dosen (her-) geben od. vergönnen*

way down F [wei] *tief unten*

pile [pail] *Haufen, Stapel*

sack [sæk] *Sack*

sweet pea [swiːt piː] *Gartenwicke, hier: Ackererbse*

it'd ['itid] = it would

just solid *sl.* [dʒʌst 'sɔlid] = just great F [greit] *einfach großartig*

smell [smel] *Duft, Geruch*

knock over [nɔk] *umwerfen*

broke *sl.* [brəuk] *pleite, bankrott, ruiniert*

'course [kɔːs] = of course

seed [siːd] *Samen Pl*

I don't give a damn [dæm] *das ist mir ganz egal*

color AE = colour BE ['kʌlə] *Farbe*

breast [brest] *Brust*

big as pillows. I'm hungry, I tell you, I'm hungry for everything, for a lot of everything."

Ed's face became grave under the shouting. "If you'd just take one of these, you'd get some sleep."

Peter looked ashamed. "I'm all right. I didn't mean to °yell like that. I'm not just thinking these things for the first time. °I been thinking about them for years, the way a °kid thinks of °vacation. I was always afraid °I'd be too old. Or that I'd go first and °miss everything. But I'm only fifty, I've got °plenty of °vinegar left. I told Emma about the sweet peas, but she wouldn't let me. I don't know how she made me do things," he said wonderingly. "I can't remember. She had a way of doing it. But she's gone. I can feel she's gone just like that harness is gone. I'm going to °slouch, Ed—slouch all over the place. I'm going to °track dirt into the house. I'm going to get a big fat °housekeeper —a big fat one from San Francisco. I'm going to have a bottle of °brandy on the °shelf all the time."

Ed Chappell stood up and stretched his arms over his head. "I guess I'll go home now, if you feel all right. °I got to get some sleep. You better °wind that clock, Peter. It °don't do a clock any good to stand not running."

The day after the funeral Peter Randall went to work on his farm. The Chappells, who lived on the next place, saw the lamp in his kitchen long before daylight, and they saw his °lantern cross the yard to the barn half an hour before they even got up.

yell AE [jel] *brüllen, schreien*

I been thinking = I have been thinking
kid *sl.* [kid] *Kind*
vacation [vəˈkeiʃən] *(Schul-) Ferien*
I'd [aid] = I would
miss [mis] *versäumen, -passen*
plenty of [ˈplenti] *viel, e-e Menge, massenhaft*
vinegar [ˈvinigə] *Schwung, Unternehmungslust*

slouch [slautʃ] *nachlässig od. vornübergebeugt gehen*
track dirt AE [træk] *hier: Schmutz(spuren) hineintragen*
housekeeper [ˈhauskiːpə] *Haushälterin*
brandy [ˈbrændi] *Branntwein, Brandy*
shelf [ʃelf] *Regal, Wandbrett*

I got to *ich muß*

wind [waind] *aufziehen*
it don't *sl.* [dəunt] = it doesn't [ˈdʌznt]

lantern [ˈlæntən] *Laterne*

55

Peter °pruned his °orchard in three days. He worked from first light until he couldn't see the °twigs against the sky any more. Then he started to °shape the big piece of river flat. He °plowed and °rolled and °harrowed. Two strange men dressed in boots and °riding breeches came out and looked at his land. They felt the dirt with their fingers and °ran a °post-hole digger deep down under the °surface, and when they went away they took little °paper bags of the dirt with them.

°Ordinarily, before °planting time, the farmers did a good deal of visiting °back and forth. They sat on their °haunches, °picking up handsful of dirt and °breaking little °clods between their fingers. They °discussed markets and crops, °recalled other years when °beans had done well in a good market, and other years when °field peas didn't bring enough to pay for the seed hardly. After a great number of these °discussions it usually happened that all the farmers °planted the same things. There were certain men whose ideas °carried weight. If Peter Randall or Clark DeWitt thought they would °put in °pink beans and °barley, most of the crops would turn out to be pink beans and barley that year; for, since such men were respected and °fairly successful, it was °conceded that their plans must °be based on something besides °chance °choice. It was generally believed but never °stated that Peter Randall and Clark DeWitt had °extra °reasoning powers and special °prophetic °knowledge.

prune [pru:n] *beschneiden*
orchard *hier: Obstbäume Pl*
twig [twig] (*dünner*) *Zweig*
shape [ʃeip] *gestalten, formen*
plow AE = plough BE [plau] *pflügen*
roll [rəul] *hier: (glatt)walzen*
harrow ['hærəu] *eggen*

riding breeches Pl ['raidiŋ 'britʃiz] *Reithose*
ran [ræn] *von* run *treiben*
post-hole digger ['pəusthəul 'digə] *Bohrmaschine*
surface ['sə:fis] (*Erd*)*Oberfläche*
paper bag ['pæpə bæg] *Tüte*
ordinarily ['ɔ:dnrili] (*für*) *gewöhnlich, normalerweise*
planting time ['pla:ntiŋ taim] *hier: Aussaat*
back and forth [fɔ:θ] *hin u. her, hier: gegenseitig*
haunches Pl ['hɔ:ntʃiz] *Gesäß, Hintern*
pick up *in die Hand nehmen*
break [breik] *hier: zerkrümeln*
clod [klɔd] *Erdklumpen*
discuss [disˈkʌs] *erörtern, sich unterhalten über*
recall [riˈkɔ:l] *sich erinnern an*
bean [bi:n] *Bohne*
field pea [fi:ld] *Ackererbse*
discussion [disˈkʌʃən] *Debatte, Besprechung*
plant [pla:nt] *anpflanzen, -bauen*
carry weight ['kæri weit] *Gewicht haben, viel gelten*
put in *anpflanzen, -bauen*
pink bean *rosablütige Gartenbohne*
barley ['ba:li] *Gerste*
fairly ['fɛəli] *ziemlich*
concede [kənˈsi:d] *einräumen, zugestehen*
be based on [beist] *beruhen od. basieren auf*
chance [tʃa:ns] *zufällig*
choice [tʃɔis] (*Aus*)*Wahl*
state [steit] *erwähnen*
extra ['ekstrə] *außergewöhnlich, besonders gut*
reasoning power ['ri:zniŋ 'pauə] *Urteilskraft*

When the usual visits started, it was seen that a change had taken place in Peter Randall. He sat on his °plow and talked pleasantly enough. He said he hadn't °decided yet what to plant, but he said it in such a °guilty way that it was °plain he didn't °intend to tell. When he had °rebuffed °a few °inquiries, the visits to his place stopped and the farmers went over °in a body to Clark DeWitt. Clark was putting in °Chevalier barley. His °decision °dictated the major part of the planting in the °vicinity.

But because the questions stopped, the interest did not. Men °driving by the forty-five acre flat of the Randall place studied the field to try to °figure out from the type of work what the crop was going to be. When Peter drove the °seeder back and forth across the land no one came in, for Peter had made it plain that his crop was a °secret.

Ed Chappell didn't °tell on him, either. Ed was a little ashamed when he thought of that night; ashamed of Peter for °breaking down, and ashamed of himself for having sat there and listened. He watched Peter °narrowly to see whether his °vicious °intentions were really there or whether the whole conversation had been the result of °loss and °hysteria. He did notice that Peter's shoulders weren't back and that his stomach stuck out a little. He went to Peter's house and was relieved when he saw no dirt on the floor and when he heard the mantel clock °ticking away.

prophetic [prə'fetik] *prophetisch*

knowledge ['nɔlidʒ] *Kenntnisse Pl, Wissen*

---

plow AE = plough BE [plau] *Pflug*

decide [di'said] *sich entscheiden od. entschließen*

guilty ['gilti] *schuldbewußt*

plain [plein] *klar, offensichtlich*

intend [in'tend] *beabsichtigen, vorhaben*

rebuff [ri'bʌf] *zurück-, abweisen*

a few [fju:] *einige, ein paar*

inquiry [in'kwaiəri] *(Nach-)Frage, Erkundigung*

in a body *zusammen, geschlossen*

Chevalier barley [ʃevə'liə] *e-e Gerstensorte*

decision [di'siʒən] *Entscheidung; Entschluß*

dictate [dik'teit] *diktieren, bestimmen*

vicinity [vi'siniti] *Nachbarschaft, Umgebung*

drive by [draiv bai] *vorbeifahren an*

figure out ['figə] *herauskommen, 'rauskriegen*

seeder ['si:də] *Sämaschine*

secret ['si:krit] *Geheimnis*

tell on s.o. *j-n verraten*

---

break down *zusammenbrechen*

narrow ['nærəu] *genau*

vicious ['viʃəs] *verwerflich*

intention [in'tenʃən] *Absicht, Vorhaben*

loss [lɔs] *Verlust*

hysteria [his'tiəriə] *Hysterie*

tick away *weiterticken*

Mrs. Chappell spoke often of the afternoon. "You'd've thought he °lost his mind the way he carried on. He just °howled. Ed stayed with him part of the night, until he °quieted down. Ed had to give him some whiskey to get him to sleep. But," she said brightly, "hard work is the thing to kill °sorrow. Peter Randall is getting up at three o'clock every morning. I can see the light in his kitchen window from my bedroom."

The °pussywillows burst out in silver drops, and the little °weeds °sprouted up along the °roadside. The Salinas River °ran dark water, flowed for a month, and then °subsided into green °pools again. Peter Randall had shaped his land beautifully. It was smooth and black; no clod was larger than a small °marble, and under the rains it looked °purple with °richness.

And then the little weak lines of green stretched out across the black field. In the °dusk a neighbor crawled under the °fence and pulled one of the °tiny plants. "Some kind of °legume," he told his friends. "Field peas, I guess. What did he want to be so quiet about it for? I asked him right out what he was planting, and he wouldn't tell me."

The word ran through the farms, "It's sweet peas. The whole °God-damn' forty-five acres is in sweet peas!" Men called on Clark DeWitt then, to get his opinion.

His opinion was this: "People think because you can get twenty to sixty cents a pound for sweet peas you can get rich on them. But it's the most

lost his mind [lɔst, maind] *von* lose one's mind [luːz] *den Verstand verlieren*
howl [haul] *heulen, weinen*
quiet down ['kwaiət] *sich beruhigen*

sorrow ['sɔrəu] *Kummer, Leid*

pussywillow ['pusiwiləu] *nordamerikanische Weidenart*
weed [wiːd] *Unkraut*
sprout up [spraut] *hervorsprießen*
roadside ['rəudsaid] *Straßen-, Wegrand*
ran [ræn] *von* run *führen*
subside into [səb'said] *hier: sich sammeln in*
pool [puːl] *Tümpel, Pfütze*
marble ['mɑːbl] *Murmel*
purple ['pəːpl] *purpurrot*
richness ['ritʃnis] *Fettigkeit (des Bodens)*

dusk [dʌsk] *(Abend)Dämmerung*
fence [fens] *Zaun, Umzäunung*
tiny ['taini] *winzig*
legume ['legjuːm] *Hülsenfrucht*

God-damn' = God-damned *sl.* ['gɔdæm(d)] *gottverdammt*

°ticklish crop in the world. If the °bugs don't get it, it might do good. And then come a hot day and °bust the °pods and lose your crop on the ground. Or it might come up a little rain and spoil °the whole kaboodle. It's all right to put in a few acres and °take a chance, but not the whole place. Peter's °touched in the head since Emma died."

This opinion was widely °distributed. Every man used it as his own. Two neighbors often said it to each other, each one °repeating half of it. When too many people said it to Peter Randall he became angry. One day he cried, "Say, whose land is this? If I want to go broke, I've got a damn good right to, haven't I?" And that changed the whole feeling. Men remembered that Peter was a good farmer. Perhaps he had special knowledge. Why, that's who those two men in boots were—soil °chemists! °A good many of the farmers wished they'd put in a few acres of sweet peas.

They wished it particularly when the °vines spread out, when they met each other across the rows and hid the dark earth from sight, when the °buds began to form and it was seen the crop was rich. And then the °blooms came; forty-five acres of color, forty-five acres of °perfume. It was said that you could smell them in Salinas, four miles away. Buses brought the school children out to look at them. A group of men from a seed °company spent all day looking at the vines and feeling the earth.

---

ticklish ['tikliʃ] *heikel, schwierig, kitz(e)lig*
bug AE [bʌg] *Insekt*
bust *sl.* [bʌst] *hier: aufbrechen lassen*
pod [pɔd] *Schote, Hülse*

the whole kaboodle = ... caboodle *sl.* [həul, kə'buːdl] *der ganze Plunder od. Kram*
take a chance [tʃɑːns] *es darauf ankommen lassen, es riskieren*
touched in the head [tʌtʃt, hed] *nicht ganz bei Trost*
distribute [dis'tribjuːt] *verbreiten, herumtragen*

repeat [ri'piːt] *wiederholen*

chemist ['kemist] *Chemiker*
a good many [gud 'meni] *ziemlich viele, e-e beträchtliche (An)Zahl*

vine [vain] *Rebe, Ranke*

bud [bʌd] *Knospe*

bloom [bluːm] *Blüte*

perfume ['pəːfjuːm] *Duft, Wohlgeruch*

company ['kʌmpəni] *Firma, Gesellschaft*

59

Peter Randall sat on his porch in a rocking chair every afternoon. He looked down on the great °squares of pink and blue, and on the mad square of mixed colors. When the afternoon breeze came up, he °inhaled deeply. His blue shirt was open at the throat, as though he wanted to get the perfume down next his skin.

Men called on Clark DeWitt to get his opinion now. He said, "There's about ten things that can happen to °spoil that crop. He's °welcome to his sweet peas." But the men knew from Clark's °irritation that he was a little °jealous. They looked up over the fields of color to where Peter sat on his porch, and they felt a new °admiration and respect for him.

Ed Chappell walked up the steps to him one afternoon. "You got a crop there, °mister."

"Looks that way," said Peter.

"I took a look. Pods are °setting fine."

Peter sighed. °"Blooming's nearly over," he said. "I'll hate to see the °petals drop off."

"Well, I'd be glad to see 'em drop. You'll °make a lot of money, if nothing happens."

Peter took out a °bandana handkerchief and °wiped his nose, and °jiggled it sideways to stop an °itch. "I'll be sorry when the smell stops," he said.

Then Ed °made his reference to the night of the death. One of his eyes °drooped °secretly. °"Found somebody to °keep house for you?"

square [skwɛə] *Quadrat, Viereck*

inhale [inˈheil] *einatmen*

spoil [spɔil] *vernichten*
be welcome to s.th. [ˈwelkəm] *et. gern behalten können*
irritation [iriˈteiʃən] *Verärgerung, Gereiztheit*
jealous [ˈdʒeləs] *eifersüchtig*

admiration [ædməˈreiʃən] *Bewunderung*

mister [ˈmistə] *hier: Meister, Chef*
set fine [fain] *hier: gut kommen*
blooming [ˈbluːmiŋ] *Blüte, Blühen*
petal [ˈpetl] *Blütenblatt*
make money [ˈmʌni] *Geld machen, gut verdienen*
bandana handkerchief [bænˈdænə ˈhæŋkətʃif] *großes buntes Taschentuch*
wipe one's nose [waip, nəuz] *sich die Nase putzen*
jiggle [ˈdʒigl] *leicht rütteln, hier: reiben*
itch [itʃ] *Juckreiz*
make reference to s.th. [ˈrefrəns] *auf et. anspielen, et. erwähnen*
droop [druːp] *hier: sich schließen*
secret [ˈsiːkrit] *verstohlen*
found somebody F [faund ˈsʌmbədi] = did you find somebody
keep house for s.o. [kiːp] *j-m den Haushalt führen*

60

"I haven't looked," said Peter. "I haven't had time." There were °lines of worry about his eyes. But who wouldn't °worry, Ed thought, when a single shower could ruin his whole year's crop.

If the year and the weather had been °manufactured for sweet peas, they couldn't have been better. The °fog lay close to the ground in the mornings when the vines were pulled. When the great piles of vines lay safely on spread °canvasses, the hot sun shone down and °crisped the pods for the °threshers. The neighbors watched the long °cotton sacks filling with round black seeds, and they went home and tried to figure out how much money Peter would make on his tremendous crop. Clark DeWitt lost a good part of his °following. The men decided to find out what Peter was going to plant next year if they had to follow him around. How did he know, for instance, that °this year'd be good for sweet peas? He *must* have some kind of special knowledge.

When a man from the upper Salinas Valley goes to San Francisco on business or for a vacation, he takes a room in the Ramona Hotel. This is a nice °arrangement, for in the °lobby he can usually find someone from home. They can sit in the soft chairs of the lobby and talk about the Salinas Valley.

Ed Chappell went to San Francisco to meet his wife's °cousin who was coming out from Ohio for a trip. °The train was not due until the next morning. In the lobby of the Ramona,

lines of worry [lainz, ˈwʌri] *Sorgenfältchen*
worry *sich Sorgen machen*

manufacture [mænjuˈfæktʃə] *anfertigen, machen*
fog [fɔg] *Nebel*

canvas [ˈkænvəs] *Zeltplane*
crisp [krisp] *hier: dörren*
thresher [ˈθreʃə] *Dreschmaschine; Drescher*
cotton sack [ˈkɔtn] *Baumwollsack*

following [ˈfɔləuiŋ] *Anhänger (-schaft)*

this year'd be [jəːd] = this year would be

arrangement [əˈreindʒmənt] *Einrichtung*
lobby AE [ˈlɔbi] *Hotelhalle*

cousin [ˈkʌzn] *Vetter*

the train was not due until ... [trein, djuː, ənˈtil] *der Zug sollte erst am ... ankommen*

61

Ed looked for someone from the Salinas Valley, but he could see only strangers sitting in the soft chairs. He went out to a °moving picture show. When he returned, he looked again for someone from home, and still there were only strangers. For a moment °he considered glancing over the °register, but it was quite late. He sat down to finish his cigar before he went to bed.

There was a °commotion at the door. Ed saw the °clerk °motion with his hand. A °bellhop ran out. Ed squirmed around in his chair to look. Outside a man was being helped out of a °taxicab. The bellhop took him from the driver and guided him in the door. It was Peter Randall. His eyes were °glassy, and his mouth open and wet. He had no hat on his °mussed hair. Ed jumped up and strode over to him.

"Peter!"

Peter was °batting helplessly at the bellhop. "Let me alone," he explained. "I'm all right. You let me alone, and I'll give you °two bits."

Ed called again, "Peter!"

The glassy eyes turned slowly to him, and then Peter fell into his arms. "My old friend," he cried. "Ed Chappell, my old, good friend. °What you doing here? Come up to my room and have a drink."

Ed set him back on his feet. "Sure I will," he said. "I'd like a little °nightcap."

"Night-cap, °hell. We'll go out and see a show, or something."

Ed helped him into the °elevator and got him to his room. Peter °dropped

moving picture show F ['mu:-viŋ, 'piktʃə ʃəu] = motion picture show ['məuʃən] *Film-vorstellung*

he considered [kən'sidəd] *e dachte daran*

register ['redʒistə] *Hotel register*

commotion [kə'məuʃən] *Auf ruhr, Tumult*

clerk AE [klɑ:k] *Empfangs chef*

motion ['məuʃən] *winken*

bellhop AE ['belhɔp] *Hotel page*

taxicab ['tæksikæb] *Taxi*

glassy ['glɑ:si] *glasig*

mussed AE [mʌst] *zerwühl*

bat [bæt] *schlagen*

two bits AE F [bits] *25 Cent*

what you doing ... = what are you doing

night-cap ['naitkæp] *Schlaf-trunk*

hell [hel] *hier: zum Teufel da-mit!*

elevator ['eliveitə] *Fahrstuhl, Aufzug*

drop to [drɔp] *(nieder)sinken auf, fallen auf*

heavily to the bed and °struggled up to a sitting position. "There's a bottle of whiskey in the bathroom. Bring me a drink, too."

Ed brought out the bottle and the glasses. "What you doing, Peter, °celebrating the crop? You must've made a pile of money."

Peter put out his °palm and °tapped it °impressively with a °forefinger. "Sure I made money—but it wasn't a bit better than °gambling. It was just like straight gambling."

"But you got the money."

Peter °scowled thoughtfully. "I might've lost my °pants," he said. "The whole time, all the year, I been worrying. It was just like gambling."

"Well, you got it, anyway."

Peter °changed the subject, then. °"I been sick," he said. "I been sick right in the taxicab. I just came from a fancy house on Van Ness °Avenue," he explained °apologetically, "I just had to come up to the city. °I'd'a busted if I hadn't come up and got some of the vinegar out of my system."

Ed looked at him curiously. Peter's head was hanging loosely between his shoulders. His beard was draggled and °rough. "Peter—" Ed began, "the night Emma—passed on, you said °you was going to—change things."

Peter's °swaying head rose up slowly. He stared °owlishly at Ed Chappell. "She didn't die °dead," he said °thickly. "She won't let me do things. She's worried me all year about those peas." His eyes were wondering. "I don't know how she does it." Then he frowned.

struggle up ['strʌgl] *sich mühsam aufrichten*

celebrate ['selibreit] *feiern*

palm [pɑːm] *Handfläche*
tap [tæp] (*leicht*) *klopfen* od. *pochen auf*
impressive [im'presiv] *hier: eindringlich*
forefinger ['fɔːfiŋgə] *Zeigefinger*
gambling ['gæmbliŋ] *Spielen, Wetten*
scowl [skaul] *finster blicken*
pants Pl AE [pænts] *Hose*

change the subject [tʃeindʒ, 'sʌbdʒikt] *das Thema wechseln, von et. anderem reden*
I been sick = I have been sick *ich mußte mich übergeben*
avenue AE ['ævinjuː] *Straße (in bestimmter Richtung verlaufend)*
apologetical [əpɔlə'dʒetikəl] *entschuldigend*
I'd'a ['aidə] = I would have

rough [rʌf] *struppig*
you was F = you were

swaying ['sweiiŋ] *schwankend, pendelnd*
owlish ['auliʃ] *eulenhaft, wie e-e Eule*
dead [ded] *restlos, völlig, hier: wirklich, ganz*
thickly ['θikli] *dumpf, mit belegter Stimme*
frown [fraun] *die Stirn runzeln*

His palm came out, and he tapped it again. "But °you mark, Ed Chappell, I won't wear that harness, and °I damn well won't ever wear it. You remember that." His head dropped forward again. But in a moment he looked up. °"I been drunk," he said °seriously. "I been to fancy houses." He °edged out confidentially toward Ed. His voice °dropped to a °heavy °whisper. "But it's all right, I'll °fix it. When I get back, you know what I'm going to do? I'm going to °put in electric lights. Emma always wanted electric lights." He °sagged sideways on the bed.

Ed Chappell stretched Peter out and undressed him before he went to his own room.

you mark [mɑ:k] *wohlge-merkt!, merke dir!*
I damn (= damned) well won't ever wear it ['evə, wɛə] *ich werde es überhaupt niemals mehr tragen (damned als bekräftigendes Füllwort)*
I been = I have been
serious ['sɪərɪəs] *ernst, feierlich*
edge out toward [edʒ, təˈwɔːd] *hier: sich näher herandrängen an*
drop *sich senken*
heavy ['hevi] *laut*
whisper ['wispe] *Flüstern*
fix AE [fiks] *(wieder) in Ordnung bringen*
put in *hier: installieren*
sag [sæg] *zusammensacken*

# The Murder

This happened a number of years ago in °Monterey °County, in central California. The Cañon del Castillo is one of those valleys in the Santa Lucia °range which lie between its many °spurs and °ridges. From the main Cañon del Castillo a number of little °arroyos °cut back into the mountains, °oak-wooded °canyons, °heavily °brushed with °poison oak and °sage. At the head of the canyon there stands a tremendous stone castle, °buttressed and °towered like those °strongholds the °Crusaders put up in the path of their °conquests. Only a close visit to the castle shows it to be a strange °accident of time and water and °erosion working on soft, °stratified sandstone. In the distance the ruined °battlements, the gates, the towers, even the arrow °slits, °require little °imagination to make out.

Below the castle, on the nearly °level °floor of the canyon, stand the old °ranch house, a °weathered and °mossy °barn and a °warped feeding-°shed for cattle. The house is °deserted; the doors, swinging on °rusted °hinges, °squeal and °bang on nights when the wind °courses down from the castle. Not many people visit the house. Sometimes a crowd of boys °tramp through the rooms, °peering into the

Monterey [mɔntə'rei] *Stadt u. Halbinsel südöstl. von San Franzisko, Kalifornien.*
county AE ['kaunti] *(Verwaltungs)Bezirk, Kreis*
range [reindʒ] *(Berg)Kette*
spur [spəː] *Ausläufer*
ridge [ridʒ] *(Gebirgs)Kamm, Grat*
arroyo AE [ə'rɔiəu] *Wasserlauf, Trockental*
cut back *eingeschnitten*
oak-wooded ['əukwudid] *mit Eichen bewachsen*
canyon ['kænjən] *Cañon, Felsschlucht*
heavy *hier: dicht*
brushed [brʌʃt] *mit Gebüsch bewachsen*
poison oak ['pɔizn əuk] *Giftsumach (Baum, Strauch)*
sage [seidʒ] *Salbei*
buttressed ['bʌtrist] *(durch Strebepfeiler) gestützt*
towered ['tauəd] *mit Türmen befestigt*
stronghold ['strɔŋhəuld] *Festung*
crusader [kruː'seidə] *Kreuzfahrer*
conquest ['kɔŋkwest] *Eroberung*
accident ['æksidənt] *Zufall, Zusammentreffen*
erosion [i'rəuʒən] *Verwitterung*
stratified ['strætifaid] *in Schichten gelagert*
battlement ['bætlmənt] *Zinnen*
slit *hier: Schießscharte*
require [ri'kwaiə] *erfordern*
imagination [imædʒi'neiʃən] *Phantasie*
level ['levl] *eben*
floor [flɔː] *(Tal)Sohle*
ranch [rɑːntʃ, AE ræntʃ] *Ranch, Viehfarm*
weathered ['weðəd] *verwittert*
mossy ['mɔsi] *moosbewachsen*

65

empty °closets and loudly °defying the ghosts they °deny.

Jim Moore, who owns the land, does not like to have people about the house. He rides up from his new house, farther down the valley, and °chases the boys away. He has put °"No Trespassing" signs on his °fences to keep curious and °morbid people out. Sometimes he thinks of burning the old house down, but then a strange and °powerful °relation with the swinging doors, the blind and °desolate windows, forbids the °destruction. If he should burn the house he would °destroy a great and important piece of his life. He knows that when he goes to town with his plump and still pretty wife, people turn and look at his °retreating back with °awe and some admiration.

Jim Moore was born in the old house and grew up in it. He knew every °grained and weathered board of the barn, every °smooth, °worn °manger-rack. His mother and father were both dead when he was thirty. He °celebrated his °majority by °raising a beard. He sold the pigs and °decided never to have any more. At last he bought a fine °Guernsey bull to °improve his °stock, and he began to go to Monterey on Saturday nights, to °get drunk and to talk with the noisy girls of the Three Star.

Within a year Jim Moore married Jelka Sepic, a °Jugo-Slav girl, daughter of a °heavy and °patient farmer of °Pine Canyon. Jim was not proud of her foreign family, of her many broth-

barn [bɑːn] *Stall; Scheune*
warped [wɔːpt] *verzogen, schief*
shed *Schuppen, Stall*
desert [diˈzəːt] *verlassen*
rusted [ˈrʌstid] *rostig*
hinge [hindʒ] *(Tür)Angel*
squeal [skwiːl] *quietschen*
bang [bæŋ] *(zu)schlagen (Tür)*
course [kɔːs] *stürmen*
tramp [træmp] *stromern*
peer [piə] *spähen*

---

closet [ˈklɔzit] *Kammer*
defy [diˈfai] *trotzen*
deny [diˈnai] *(ver)leugnen*
chase [tʃeis] *jagen*
no trespassing [ˈtrespəsiŋ] *Betreten verboten*
fence [fens] *Zaun*
morbid [ˈmɔːbid] *(hier: moralisch) krankhaft*
powerful [ˈpauəful] *mächtig*
relation [riˈleiʃən] *Beziehung*
desolate [ˈdesəlit] *trostlos, öde*
destruction [disˈtrʌkʃən] *Zerstörung*
destroy [disˈtrɔi] *zerstören*
retreat [riˈtriːt] *sich entfernen*
awe [ɔː] *Ehrfurcht*

---

grained [greind] *gemasert*
smooth [smuːθ] *glatt*
worn [wɔːn] *abgewetzt*
manger-rack [ˈmeindʒəræk] *Futterraufe*
celebrate [ˈselibreit] *feiern*
majority [məˈdʒɔriti] *Volljährigkeit*
raise a beard [reiz, biəd] *sich e-n Bart wachsen lassen*
decide [diˈsaid] *beschließen*
Guernsey [ˈgəːnzi] *Guernsey (-rind)*
improve [imˈpruːv] *verbessern*
stock [stɔk] *Vieh(bestand)*
get drunk [drʌŋk] *sich betrinken*

---

Jugo-Slav = Yugoslav [ˈjuːgəuˈslɑːv] *jugoslawisch*
heavy [ˈhevi] *hier: behäbig*
patient [ˈpeiʃənt] *hier: gelassen*
pine [pain] *Kiefer, Pinie*

ers and sisters and cousins, but he °delighted in her beauty. Jelka had eyes as large and questioning as a °doe's eyes. Her nose was thin and sharply °faceted, and her lips were °deep and soft. Jelka's skin always °startled Jim, for between night and night he forgot how beautiful it was. She was so °smooth and quiet and gentle, such a good °housekeeper, that Jim often thought with °disgust of her father's °advice on the °wedding day. The old man, °bleary and °bloated with festival beer, °elbowed Jim in the ribs and grinned °suggestively, so that his little dark eyes almost disappeared behind °puffed and °wrinkled lids.

°"Don't be big fool, now," he said. "Jelka is °Slav girl. °He's not like American girl. If he is bad, beat him. If he's good too long, beat him too. I beat his °mama. °Papa beat my mama. Slav girl! °He's not like a man that don't °beat hell out of him."

"I wouldn't beat Jelka," Jim said.

The father °giggled and °nudged him again with his elbow. "Don't be big fool," he warned. °"Sometime you see." He °rolled back to the beer °barrel.

Jim found soon enough that Jelka was not like American girls. She was very quiet. She never spoke first, but only answered his questions, and then with soft short °replies. She learned her husband as she learned °passages of °Scripture. After they had been married a while, Jim never wanted for any °habitual thing in the house °but Jelka had it ready for him before he could ask. She was a fine wife, but °there

delight in [di'lait] *entzückt sein von*

doe [dəu] *Reh(geiß)*

faceted ['fæsitid] *hier: geschnitten*
deep [di:p] *hier: voll*
startle ['stɑːtl] *überraschen*

smooth [smu:θ] *ausgeglichen*

housekeeper ['hauski:pə] *Haushälterin*
disgust [dis'gʌst] *Abscheu, Empörung*
advice [əd'vais] *Rat(schlag)*
wedding ['wediŋ] *Hochzeits...*
bleary ['bliəri] *benommen*
bloated ['bləutid] *aufgedunsen*
elbow ['elbəu] *mit dem Ellenbogen (an)stoßen*
suggestive [sə'dʒestiv] *vielsagend*
puffed [pʌft] *geschwollen*
wrinkled ['riŋkld] *faltig*
don't be big fool *sl. sei nicht blöd*
Slav [slɑːv] = Yugoslav
he *für* she
mamma [mə'mɑː] *Mama*
papa [pə'pɑː] *Papa*
he's not like a man *sl. das ist kein richtiger Mann, der ...*
beat hell out of F [bi:t] *nach Strich und Faden verdreschen*
giggle ['gigl] *kichern*
nudge [nʌdʒ] *anstoßen, stupsen*
sometime you see *sl. du wirst schon (noch) sehen*
roll [rəul] *schlingern, unsicher gehen*
barrel ['bærəl] *Faß*

reply [ri'plai] *Antwort*
passage ['pæsidʒ] *(Text)Stelle*
Scripture ['skriptʃə] *(Heilige) Schrift, Bibel*
habitual [hə'bitjuəl] *gewohnt, üblich*
but she had it ready for him ['redi] *was sie nicht schon für ihn bereit hatte*

67

was no companionship in her. She never talked. Her great eyes followed him, and when he smiled, sometimes she smiled too, a distant and °covered smile. Her °knitting and °mending and °sewing were °interminable. There she sat, watching her °wise hands, and she seemed to regard with °wonder and °pride the little white hands that could do such nice and useful things. She was so much like an animal that sometimes Jim °patted her head and neck under the same °impulse that made him °stroke a horse.

In the house Jelka was °remarkable. °No matter what time Jim came in from the hot dry range or from the °bottom farm land, his dinner was °exactly, steamingly ready for him. She watched while he °ate, and °pushed the °dishes close when he needed them, and filled his cup when it was empty.

Early in the °marriage he told her things that happened on the farm, but she smiled at him as a °foreigner does who wishes to be °agreeable even though he doesn't understand.

"The °stallion cut himself on the °barbed wire," he said.

And she replied, "Yes," with a downward °inflection that held neither question nor interest.

He °realized before long that he could not °get in touch with her in any way. If she had a life °apart, it was so °remote as to be °beyond his reach. The °barrier in her eyes was not one that could be °removed, for it was neither °hostile nor °intentional.

---

there was no companionship in her [kəmˈpænjənʃip] *er hatte keine Gesellschaft an ihr*

covered [ˈkʌvəd] *versteckt*

knitting [ˈnitiŋ] *Stricken*
mending [ˈmendiŋ] *Flicken, Ausbessern*
sewing [ˈsəuiŋ] *Nähen*
interminable [inˈtə:minəbl] *endlos*
wise [waiz] *erfahren*
wonder [ˈwʌndə] *Staunen*
pride [praid] *Stolz*

pat [pæt] *tätscheln*

impulse [ˈimpʌls] *Antrieb*

stroke [strəuk] *streicheln*

remarkable [riˈmɑ:kəbl] *außerordentlich*
no matter *ganz gleich*
bottom ... land [ˈbɔtəm] *Schwemmland*

exactly [igˈzæktli] *pünktlich*

ate [et, eit] *von* eat [i:t] *essen*
push close [puʃ kləus] *näherschieben*
dish [diʃ] *Schüssel*

marriage [ˈmæridʒ] *Ehe*

foreigner [ˈfɔrinə] *Fremder, Ausländer*
agreeable [əˈgri:əbl] *liebenswürdig*
stallion [ˈstæljən] *(Zucht)Hengst*
barbed wire [bɑ:bd ˈwaiə] *Stacheldraht*
inflection [inˈflekʃən] *(Satz-) Melodie*
realize [ˈriəlaiz] *sich klarmachen*
get in touch with [tʌtʃ] *Zugang finden zu*
apart [əˈpɑ:t] *einzeln, für sich*
remote [riˈməut] *fern*
beyond his reach [biˈjɔnd] *ihm unerreichbar*
barrier [ˈbæriə] *Schranke*
remove [riˈmu:v] *beseitigen, aus dem Weg räumen*
hostile [ˈhɔstail] *feindselig*
intentional [inˈtenʃənl] *absichtlich*

At night he stroked her °straight black hair and her °unbelievably smooth golden shoulders, and she °whimpered a little °with pleasure. Only in the °climax of his °embrace did she seem to have a life apart, °fierce and °passionate. And then °immediately she °lapsed into the °alert and °painfully °dutiful wife.

"Why don't you ever talk to me?" he °demanded. "Don't you want to talk to me?"

"Yes," she said. "What do you want me to say?" She spoke the language of his race out of a °mind that was foreign to his race.

When a year had passed, Jim began to °crave the company of women, the °chattery °exchange of °small talk, the shrill °pleasant °insults, the °shame-sharpened °vulgarity. He began to go again to town, to drink and to play with the noisy girls of the Three Star. They liked him there °for his °firm, °controlled face and for his °readiness to laugh.

"Where's your wife?" they demanded.

"Home in the barn," he responded. It was a °never-failing °joke.

Saturday afternoons he saddled a horse and put a °rifle in the °scabbard in case he should see a °deer. Always he asked, "You °don't mind staying alone?"

"No. °I don't mind."

At once he asked, °""Suppose someone should come?"

| | |
|---|---|
| straight [streit] | *glatt* |
| unbelievable [ʌnbi'li:vəbl] | *unglaublich* |
| whimper ['wimpə] | *winseln, wimmern* |
| with pleasure ['pleʒə] | *vor Freude* |
| climax ['klaimæks] | *Höhepunkt* |
| embrace [im'breis] | *Umarmung* |
| fierce [fiəs] | *wild, heftig* |
| passionate ['pæʃənit] | *leidenschaftlich* |
| immediately [i'mi:djətli] | *sofort* |
| lapse [læps] | *verfallen, abgleiten* |
| alert [ə'lə:t] | *flink* |
| painfully ['peinfuli] | *übertrieben* |
| dutiful ['dju:tiful] | *pflichtbewußt* |
| demand [di'ma:nd] | *fragen* |
| mind [maind] | *Seele, Gemüt* |
| crave [kreiv] | *suchen, ersehnen* |
| chattery ['tʃætəri] | *geschwätzig* |
| exchange [iks'tʃeindʒ] | *Austausch* |
| small talk [tɔ:k] | *belangloses Geplauder* |
| pleasant ['pleznt] | *freundlich* |
| insult ['insʌlt] | *Anzüglichkeit, Frechheit* |
| shame-sharpened ['ʃeimʃɑ:pənd] | *durch das Schamgefühl stärker empfunden* |
| vulgarity [vʌl'gæriti] | *Gewöhnlichkeit* |
| for [fɔ:] | *wegen* |
| firm [fə:m] | *entschlossen* |
| controlled [kən'trəuld] | *beherrscht* |
| readiness ['redinis] | *Bereitschaft* |
| never-failing [nevə'feiliŋ] | *unfehlbar* |
| joke [dʒəuk] | *Witz* |
| rifle ['raifl] | *Gewehr* |
| scabbard ['skæbəd] | *Scheide, Halterung* |
| deer [diə] | *Reh(wild)* |
| I don't mind [dəunt maind] | *es macht mir nichts aus* |
| suppose [sə'pəuz] | *angenommen* |

Her eyes °sharpened for a moment, and then she smiled. "I would send them away," she said.

"I'll be back about °noon tomorrow. It's too far to ride in the night." He felt that she knew where he was going, but she never protested nor gave any sign of °disapproval. "You should have a baby," he said.

Her face lighted up. "Some time God will be good," she said °eagerly.

He was sorry for her °loneliness. If only she visited with the other women of the canyon she would be less lonely, but she had no °gift for visiting. Once every month or so she put horses to the °buckboard and went to °spend an afternoon with her mother, and with the °brood of brothers and sisters and °cousins who lived in her father's house.

"A fine time you'll have," Jim said to her. "You'll °gabble your °crazy language like °ducks for a whole afternoon. You'll giggle with that big grown cousin of yours with the °embarrassed face. If I could °find any fault with you, I'd call you a °damn foreigner." He remembered how he °blessed the bread with the sign of the cross before she put it in the °oven, how she °knelt at the bedside every night, how she had a holy picture °tacked to the wall in the closet.

One Saturday of a hot dusty June, Jim cut °oats in the °farm flat. The day was long. It was after six o'clock when the °mower °tumbled the last °band of oats. He °drove the °clanking machine up into the °barnyard and °backed it

sharpen ['ʃɑːpən] *scharf blicken*

noon [nuːn] *Mittag*

disapproval [disə'pruːvəl] *Mißbilligung*

eager ['iːgə] *eifrig*
loneliness ['ləunlinis] *Einsamkeit*

gift *Gabe, Begabung*

buckboard AE ['bʌkbɔːd] *leichter vierrädriger Wagen*
spend *verbringen*
brood [bruːd] *Sippe*
cousin ['kʌzn] *Vetter*

gabble ['gæbl] *schnattern*
crazy ['kreizi] *verrückt*
duck [dʌk] *Ente*
embarrassed [im'bærəst] *verlegen, betreten*
find fault with [fɔːlt] *et. auszusetzen haben an*
damn [dæm] *verdammt*
bless [bles] *segnen*
oven ['ʌvn] *Backofen*
knelt [nelt] *von* kneel [niːl] *knien*
tack [tæk] *anheften*
oats *Pl* [əuts] *Hafer*
farm flat AE [fɑːm flæt] *ebenes Feld*
mower ['məuə] *Mähmaschine*
tumble ['tʌmbl] *schleudern*
band [bænd] *Garbe*
drove [drəuv] *von* drive [draiv] *fahren*
clanking ['klæŋkiŋ] *rasselnd*
barnyard ['bɑːnjɑːd] *(Scheunen)Hof*
back *rückwärts fahren*

into the °implement shed, and there he °unhitched the horses and °turned them out to °graze on the hills over Sunday. When he entered the kitchen Jelka was just putting his dinner on the table. He washed his hands and face and sat down to eat.

"I'm tired," he said, "but I think I'll go to Monterey °anyway. There'll be a full moon."

Her soft eyes smiled.

"I'll tell you what I'll do," he said. "If you would like to go, I'll °hitch up a °rig and take you with me."

She smiled again and shook her head. "No, the °stores would be closed. I would °rather stay here."

"Well, all right, I'll saddle the horse then. I didn't think I was going. The stock's all turned out. Maybe I can catch a horse easy. Sure you don't want to go?"

"If it was early, and I could go to the stores—but it will be ten o'clock when you get there."

"Oh, no—well, anyway, °on horseback I'll make it a little after nine."

Her mouth smiled to itself, but her eyes watched him for the °development of a wish. Perhaps because he was tired from the long day's work, he demanded, "What are you thinking about?"

"Thinking about? I remember, °you used to ask that nearly every day when we were first married."

"But what are you?" he insisted °irritably.

"Oh—I'm thinking about the eggs under the black °hen." She got up and went to the big °calendar on the wall.

---

implement ['implimənt] *Gerät;
  Geräte...*
unhitch ['ʌn'hitʃ] *ausspannen*
turn out [tə:n] *auf die Weide
  treiben*
graze [greiz] *grasen, weiden*

anyway ['eniwei] *trotzdem*

hitch up [hitʃ] *anspannen*
rig AE F [rig] *Gespann*

store AE [stɔ:] *Laden, Geschäft*
rather ['rɑ:ðə] *lieber*

on horseback ['hɔ:sbæk] *zu
  Pferd, mit dem Pferd*

development [di'veləpmənt]
  *Entwicklung*

you used to [ju:st] *du hast
  immer*

irritable ['iritəbl] *gereizt*

hen *Henne*
calendar ['kælində] *Kalender*

---

71

"They will °hatch tomorrow or maybe Monday."

It was almost °dusk when he had finished °shaving and putting on his blue °serge °suit and his new boots. Jelka had the dishes washed and put away. As Jim went through the kitchen he saw that she had taken the lamp to the table near the window, and that she sat beside it knitting a brown wool °sock.

"Why do you sit there tonight?" he asked. "You always sit over here. You do °funny things sometimes."

Her eyes °arose slowly from her flying hands. "The moon," she said quietly. "You said it would be full tonight. I want to see the moon °rise."

"But you're °silly. You can't see it from that window. I thought you knew °direction better than that."

She smiled °remotely. "I will look out of the bedroom window, then."

Jim put on his black hat and went out. Walking through the dark empty barn, he took a °halter from the rack. On the grassy °sidehill he °whistled high and shrill. The horses stopped °feeding and moved slowly in towards him, and stopped twenty feet away. °Carefully he °approached his °bay °gelding and moved his hand from its °rump along its side and up and over its °neck. The halter-°strap °clicked in its °buckle. Jim turned and °led the horse back to the barn. He °threw his saddle on and °cinched it °tight, put his °silver-bound °bridle over the stiff ears, buckled the °throat latch, °knotted the °tie-rope about the gelding's neck and fastened the °neat coil-

hatch [hætʃ] *ausschlüpfen*

dusk [dʌsk] *(Abend)Dämme-rung*
shaving ['ʃeiviŋ] *Rasieren*
serge [sə:dʒ] *Serge (Gewebeart)*
suit [sju:t] *Anzug*

sock [sɔk] *Socke*

funny ['fʌni] *komisch*

arose AE [ə'rəuz] *von* arise [ə'raiz] *(sich) (er)heben*

rise [raiz] *aufgehen*
silly ['sili] *dumm*
direction [di'rekʃən] *Richtung*
remote [ri'məut] *vage*
halter ['hɔ:ltə] *(Stall)Halfter*
sidehill AE ['said'hil] = hill-side BE ['hilsaid] *(Berg)Hang*
whistle ['wisl] *pfeifen*
feed [fi:d] *fressen, weiden*
careful ['keəful] *vorsichtig*
approach [ə'prəutʃ] *sich nähern*
bay [bei] *rotbraun*
gelding ['geldiŋ] *Wallach*
rump [rʌmp] *Hinterteil*
neck [nek] *Hals*
strap [stræp] *Riemen, Gurt*
click [klik] *klicken, einschnappen*
buckle ['bʌkl] *Schnalle; (fest-) schnallen*
led [led] *von* lead [li:d] *führen*
threw [θru:] *von* throw [θrəu] *werfen*
cinch AE [sintʃ] *(fest)schnallen*
tight [tait] *fest*
silver-bound ['silvəbaund] *silberbeschlagen*
bridle ['braidl] *Zaumzeug*
throat latch AE [θrəut lætʃ] *Kehlriemen*
knot [nɔt] *(ver)knoten*
tie-rope AE ['tairəup] *Anbinde-riemen*
neat coil-end [ni:t 'kɔilend] *hier: sauber aufgerolltes En-de (des Riemens)*

end to the °saddle string. Then he °slipped the halter and led the horse to the house. A °radiant crown of soft red light lay over the eastern hills. The full moon would rise before the valley had °completely lost the daylight.

In the kitchen Jelka still knitted by the window. Jim °strode to the corner of the room and took up his 30–30 °carbine. As he °rammed °cartridges into the °magazine, he said, "The moon °glow is on the hills. If you are going to see it rise, you better go outside now. It's going to be a good red one at rising."

"In a moment," she replied, "when I come to the end here." He went to her and patted her °sleek head.

"Good night. I'll °probably be back °by noon tomorrow." Her °dusky black eyes followed him out of the door.

Jim °thrust the rifle into his saddle-scabbard, and °mounted and °swung his horse down the canyon. On his right, from behind the °blackening hills, the great red moon °slid rapidly up. The double light of the day's last °afterglow and the rising moon °thickened the °outlines of the trees and gave a °mysterious new °perspective to the hills. The °dusty oaks shimmered and glowed, and the °shade under them was black as °velvet. A huge, °long-legged shadow of a horse and half a man rode to the left and °slightly °ahead of Jim. From the ranches near and distant came the sound of dogs °tuning up for a night of song. And the °roosters °crowed, thinking a new °dawn had come too quickly.

saddle string ['sædl striŋ] *vom Cowboysattel lose herabhängender dünner Lederriemen*
slip *hier: abstreifen*
radiant ['reidjənt] *strahlend*

completely [kəm'pliːtli] *völlig, vollständig*

strode [stroud] *von* stride [straid] *schreiten*
carbine ['kɑːbain] *Karabiner*
ram [ræm] *(hinein)drücken, einlegen*
cartridge ['kɑːtridʒ] *Patrone*
magazine [mægə'ziːn] *Magazin*
glow [glou] *leuchtender Schein*
sleek [sliːk] *(mit) glatt(em Haar)*
probable ['prɔbəbl] *wahrscheinlich*
by *bis zu*
dusky ['dʌski] *schwärzlich, dunkel*
thrust [θrʌst] *stoßen, stecken*
mount [maunt] *Pferd besteigen, aufsitzen*
swung [swʌŋ] *von* swing [swiŋ] *hier: (ein)schwenken lassen*
blacken ['blækən] *dunkel werden*
slid [slid] *von* slide [slaid] *gleiten*
afterglow ['ɑːftəglou] *Nachglühen, Abendrot*
thicken ['θikən] *verstärken*
outline ['autlain] *Umriß*
mysterious [mis'tiəriəs] *geheimnisvoll*
perspective [pə'spektiv] *Aussehen*
dusty ['dʌsti] *staubig*
shade [ʃeid] *Schatten*
velvet ['velvit] *Samt*
long-legged ['lɔŋlegd] *langbeinig*
slight [slait] *gering(fügig)*
ahead [ə'hed] *vor(aus)*
tune up [tjuːn] *einsetzen, einstimmen*
rooster ['ruːstə] *(Haus)Hahn*
crow [krou] *krähen*
dawn [dɔːn] *Morgendämmerung*

Jim °lifted the gelding to a trot. The °spattering °hoof-steps °echoed back from the castle behind him. He thought of °blond May at the Three Star in Monterey. "I'll be late. Maybe someone else'll have her," he thought. The moon was °clear of the hills now.

Jim had gone a mile when he heard the °hoofbeats of a horse coming towards him. A horseman °cantered up and °pulled to a stop. °"That you, Jim?"

"Yes. Oh, hello, George."

"I was just riding up to your °place. I want to tell you—you know the °springhead at the upper end of my land?"

"Yes, I know."

"Well, I was up there this afternoon. I found a °dead °campfire and a °calf's head and feet. The °skin was in the fire, half burned, but I pulled it out and it had your °brand."

°"The hell," said Jim. "How old was the fire?"

"The ground was still warm in the °ashes. °Last night, I °guess. Look, Jim, I can't go up with you. I've got to go to town, but I thought I'd tell you, so you could °take a look around."

Jim asked quietly, "Any °idea how many men?"

"No. I didn't °look close."

"Well, I guess I better go up and look. I was going to town too. But if there are °thieves working, I don't want to lose any more stock. I'll °cut up through your land if you don't °mind, George."

lift to a trot [trɔt] *hier: in Trab setzen*
spatter ['spætə] *prasseln, trappeln*
hoof-step ['huːfstep] *Huftritt*
echo ['ekəu] *widerhallen*
blond(e) [blɔnd] *blond*

clear of the hills [kliə] *ganz aus den Hügeln emporgestiegen*

hoofbeat ['huːfbiːt] *Hufschlag*
canter up ['kæntə] *herangaloppieren*
pull to a stop [stɔp] *hier: sein Pferd zum Stehen bringen*
that you? F = is that you? *bist du's?*
place [pleis] *hier: Haus, Hof*

springhead ['spriŋhed] *Quelle*

dead [ded] *erloschen*
campfire ['kæmpfaiə] *Lagerfeuer*
calf [kɑːf] *Kalb*
skin [skin] *Fell*
brand [brænd] *Brandzeichen*
the hell *zum Teufel*

ashes Pl ['æʃiz] *Asche*
last night *gestern abend*
guess AE [ges] *annehmen, denken*
take a look around *sich (ein wenig) umsehen*
idea [ai'diːə] *Ahnung, Vorstellung*
look close [kləus] *genau hinsehen*

thieves Pl [θiːvz] *von* thief [θiːf] *Dieb*
cut up *abkürzen (Weg)*
mind [maind] *etwas dagegen haben*

74

"I'd go with you, but I've got to go to town. You got a °gun with you?"

"Oh yes, sure. Here under my leg. Thanks for telling me."

"That's all right. Cut through any place you want. Good night." The °neighbor turned his horse and cantered back in the direction from which he had come.

For a few moments Jim sat in the moonlight, looking down at his °stilted shadow. He pulled his rifle from its scabbard, °levered a cartridge into the chamber, and held the gun across the °pommel of his saddle. He turned left from the road, went up the little ridge, through the oak °grove, over the °grassy °hogback and down the other side into the next canyon.

In half an hour he had found the deserted camp. He turned over the heavy, °leathery calf's head and felt its dusty tongue to °judge by the dryness how long it had been dead. He °lighted a °match and looked at his brand on the half-burned hide. At last he mounted his horse again, rode over the °bald grassy hills and °crossed into his own land.

A warm summer wind was blowing on the °hilltops. The moon, as it °quartered up the sky, lost its redness and °turned the color of strong tea. Among the hills the °coyotes were °singing, and the dogs at the ranch houses below °joined them with °broken-hearted °howling. The dark green oaks below and the yellow summer grass showed their colors in the moonlight.

gun [gʌn] *Gewehr*

neighbo(u)r ['neibə] *Nachbar*

stilted ['stiltid] *hier: langbeinig*

lever a cartridge into the chamber ['liːvə, 'tʃeimbə] *hier: durchladen*
pommel ['pʌml] *(Sattel)Knauf*

grove [grəuv] *Hain, Wäldchen*
grassy ['graːsi] *grasbewachsen*
hogback ['hɔgbæk] *langer, scharfer Bergkamm*

leathery ['leðəri] *lederartig*
judge by [dʒʌdʒ] *(be)urteilen nach*
light [lait] *anzünden*
match [mætʃ] *Streichholz*

bald [bɔːld] *kahl*
cross into [krɔs] *hier: hinüberreiten zu*
hilltop ['hiltɔp] *Hügel-, Bergspitze*
quarter up the sky ['kwɔːtə, skai] *am Himmel hinaufziehen*
turn the colo(u)r of *die Farbe von ... annehmen*
coyote ['kɔiəut] *Prärie-, Steppenwolf, Kojote*
sing *hier: heulen*
join [dʒɔin] *einstimmen, einfallen in*
broken-hearted ['brəukən-'haːtid] *herzzerbrechend*
howling ['haulɪŋ] *Heulen, Geheul*

75

Jim followed the °sound of the °cowbells to his °herd, and found them eating quietly, and a few deer feeding with them. He listened for the sound of hoofbeats or the voices of men on the wind.

It was after eleven when he turned his horse towards home. He °rounded the west tower of the sandstone castle, rode through the shadow and out into the moonlight again. Below, the roofs of his barn and house °shone °dully. The bedroom window °cast back a °streak of °reflection.

The feeding horses °lifted their heads as Jim came down through the °pasture. Their eyes °glinted redly when they turned their heads.

Jim had almost reached the °corral fence—he heard a horse stamping in the barn. His hand °jerked the gelding down. He listened. It came again, the stamping from the barn. Jim lifted his rifle and °dismounted °silently. He turned his horse °loose and °crept towards the barn.

In the blackness he could hear the °grinding of the horse's teeth as it °chewed °hay. He moved along the barn until he came to the °occupied °stall. After a moment of listening he °scratched a match on the °butt of his rifle. A °saddled and °bridled horse was °tied in the stall. The °bit was °slipped under the °chin and the °cinch °loosened. The horse stopped eating and turned its head towards the light.

Jim °blew out the match and walked quickly out of the barn. He sat on the °edge of the horse °trough and looked

sound [saund] *Klang*
cowbell ['kaubel] *Kuhglocke*
herd [həːd] *Herde*

round [raund] *hier: herumreiten um*

shone [ʃɔn] *von* shine [ʃain] *scheinen*
dull [dʌl] *matt*
cast [kɑːst] *werfen*
streak [striːk] *Streifen*
reflection [ri'flekʃən] *Widerschein*
lift *heben*
pasture ['pɑːstʃə] *Weideland*
glint [glint] *glitzern, funkeln*
corral [kɔ'rɑːl, AE kə'ræl] *Pferch*

jerk down [dʒəːk] *ruckartig halten (lassen)*

dismount [dis'maunt] *absitzen*
silent ['sailənt] *still, lautlos*
loose [luːs] *los*
crept [krept] *von* creep [kriːp] *kriechen, schleichen*
grinding ['graindiŋ] *Mahlen*
chew [tʃuː] *kauen*
hay [hei] *Heu*
occupied ['ɔkjupaid] *besetzt*
stall [stɔːl] *(Stall)Box*
scratch [skrætʃ] *anreißen*
butt [bʌt] *Kolben*
saddled ['sædld] *gesattelt*
bridled ['braidld] *gezäumt*
tie [tai] *(an)binden*
bit *Gebiß (am Zaum)*
slip *(ab-, herunter)streifen*
chin [tʃin] *Kinn*
cinch AE [sintʃ] *Sattelgurt*
loosen ['luːsn] *lösen, lockern*
blew [bluː] *von* blow [bləu] *blasen*
edge [edʒ] *Rand*
trough [trɔf] *Trog*

into the water. His thoughts came so slowly that he put them into words and said them °under his breath.

"Shall I look through the window? No. My head would throw a shadow in the room."

He °regarded the rifle in his hand. Where it had been °rubbed and °handled, the black gun °finish had °worn off, leaving the metal silvery.

At last he stood up with °decision and moved towards the house. At the °steps, an °extended foot °tried each board °tenderly before he put his °weight on it. The three ranch dogs came out from under the house and shook themselves, stretched and °sniffed, °wagged their °tails and went back to bed.

The kitchen was dark, but Jim knew where every °piece of furniture was. He put out his hand and touched the corner of the table, a chair °back, the towel hanger, as he went along. He crossed the room so silently that even he could hear only his °breath and the °whisper of his trouser legs together, and the °beating of his watch in his pocket. The bedroom door stood open and °spilled a °patch of moonlight on the kitchen floor. Jim reached the door at last and peered through.

The moonlight lay on the white bed. Jim saw Jelka lying on her back, one soft °bare arm °flung across her °forehead and eyes. He could not see who the man was, for his head was turned away. Jim watched, °holding his breath. Then Jelka °twitched in her sleep and the man rolled his head and

under his breath [breθ] *flüsternd*

regard [ri'gɑːd] *betrachten*
rub [rʌb] *(ab)reiben*
handle ['hændl] *hier: oft anfassen*
finish ['finiʃ] *Brünierung*
worn off [wɔːn] *von* wear off [weə] *(sich) abnutzen*
decision [di'siʒən] *Entschlossenheit*
step *Stufe*
extended [iks'tendid] *ausgestreckt*
try [trai] *ausprobieren*
tender ['tendə] *hier: vorsichtig*
weight [weit] *Gewicht*
sniff *schnuppern*
wag [wæg] *wedeln mit*
tail [teil] *Schwanz*

piece of furniture [piːs, 'fəːnitʃə] *Möbelstück*

back *Lehne*

breath [breθ] *Atem*

whisper ['wispə] *Wispern, hier: Rascheln*
beating ['biːtiŋ] *Klopfen, hier: Ticken*
spill [spil] *(ver)streuen*
patch [pætʃ] *Fleck*

bare [beə] *nackt, bloß*
flung [flʌŋ] *von* fling [fliŋ] *werfen*
forehead ['fɔrid] *Stirn*
hold one's breath [həuld] *den Atem anhalten*
twitch [twitʃ] *zucken*

°sighed—Jelka's cousin, her grown, embarrassed cousin.

Jim turned and quickly °stole back across the kitchen and down the back steps. He walked up the yard to the water-trough again, and sat down on the edge of it. The moon was white as °chalk, and it swam in the water, and lighted the °straws and °barley °dropped by the horses' mouths. Jim could see the mosquito °wigglers, °tumbling up and down, end over end, in the water, and he could see a °newt lying in the °sun moss in the bottom of the trough.

He °cried a few dry, hard, smothered sobs, and °wondered why, for his thought was of the grassed hilltops and of the lonely summer wind °whisking along.

His thought turned to the way his mother used to hold a °bucket to catch the °throat blood when his father killed a pig. She stood as far away as possible and held the bucket °at arms'-length to keep her clothes from getting °spattered.

Jim °dipped his hand into the trough and °stirred the moon to broken, °swirling °streams of light. He °wetted his forehead with his °damp hands and stood up. This time he did not move so quietly, but he crossed the kitchen °on tiptoe and stood in the bedroom door. Jelka moved her arm and opened her eyes a little. Then the eyes °sprang wide, then they °glistened °with moisture. Jim looked into her eyes; his face was °empty of expression. A little drop ran out of Jelka's nose and °lodged in the

---

sigh [sai] *seufzen*

stole [stəul] *von* steal [sti:l] (*sich da*von)*stehlen*

chalk [tʃɔːk] *Kreide*

straw [strɔː] *Stroh(halm)*
barley ['bɑːli] *Gerste*
drop [drɔp] *fallen (lassen)*
wiggler ['wiglə] (*Stechmücken-*) *Larve*
tumble ['tʌmbl] *taumeln*
newt [njuːt] *Wassermolch*
sun moss [sʌn mɔs] *Wasserportulak*

cry a few smothered sobs ['smʌðəd sɔbz] *ein paarmal unterdrückt aufschluchzen*
wonder why ['wʌndə] *sich nach dem Grund fragen*
whisk [wisk] *huschen, säuseln*

bucket ['bʌkit] *Eimer, Kübel*
throat [θrəut] *Kehle*

at arms' length [leŋθ] *mit ausgestreckten Armen*

spatter ['spætə] *bespritzen*
dip (*ein*)*tauchen*
stir [stəː] *um-, aufrühren*
swirling ['swəːliŋ] *wirbelnd*
stream [striːm] *hier: (Licht-) Streif*
wet *befeuchten, benetzen*
damp [dæmp] *feucht*
on tiptoe ['tiptəu] *auf Zehenspitzen*
sprang wide [spræŋ waid] *von* spring wide [spriŋ] *sich plötzlich weit öffnen*
glisten ['glisn] *glitzern, glänzen*
with moisture ['mɔistʃə] *vor Feuchtigkeit, feucht*
empty of expression [iks'preʃən] *ausdruckslos*
lodge [lɔdʒ] *hier: sich festsetzen*

°hollow of her upper lip. She °stared back at him.

Jim °cocked the rifle. The °steel °click °sounded through the house. The man on the bed °stirred °uneasily in his sleep. Jim's hands were °quivering. He °raised the gun to his shoulder and held it tightly °to keep from shaking. Over the °sights he saw the little white °square between the man's °brows and hair. The °front sight °wavered a moment and then came to °rest.

The gun °crash °tore the air. Jim, still looking down the °barrel, saw the whole bed °jolt under the °blow. A small, black, °bloodless hole was in the man's forehead. But behind, the °hollow-point took °brain and °bone and °splashed them on the °pillow.

Jelka's cousin °gurgled in his throat. His hands came °crawling out from under the °covers like big white °spiders, and they walked for a moment, then °shuddered and °fell quiet.

Jim looked slowly back at Jelka. Her nose was running. Her eyes had moved from him to the end of the rifle. She °whined °softly, like a cold °puppy.

Jim turned in panic. His °boot heels beat on the kitchen floor, but outside, he moved slowly towards the water-trough again. There was a °taste of salt in his throat, and his heart °heaved painfully. He pulled his hat off and dipped his head into the water. Then he °leaned over and °vomited on the ground. In the house he could hear Jelka moving about. She whimpered like a puppy. Jim °straightened up, weak and °dizzy.

hollow ['hɔləu] *Vertiefung, Mulde*
stare [stɛə] *starren*
cock [kɔk] *spannen (Gewehrhahn)*
steel [sti:l] *stählern, hier: metallisch*
click [klik] *Klicken*
sound [saund] *(er)tönen, zu hören sein*
stir [stə:] *sich rühren*
uneasy [un'i:zi] *unruhig*
quiver ['kwivə] *zittern*
raise [reiz] *heben*
to keep from shaking ['ʃeikiŋ] *damit es nicht zittert*
sights *Pl* [saits] *Kimme u. Korn*
square [skwɛə] *Rechteck*
brow [brau] *(Augen)Braue*
front sight [frʌnt] *Korn*
waver ['weivə] *schwanken*
rest [rest] *Ruhe*
crash [kræʃ] *Krachen*
tore [tɔ:] *von* tear [tɛə] *zerreißen*
barrel ['bærəl] *Lauf*
jolt [dʒəult] *rütteln*
blow [bləu] *Schlag*
bloodless ['blʌdlis] *blutlos, unblutig*
the hollow-point took ['hɔləupɔint] *an der Austrittsstelle des Geschosses trat(en) . . . aus*
brain [brein] *Hirn(masse)*
bone [bəun] *Knochen*
splash [splæʃ] *spritzen*
pillow ['piləu] *Kissen*
gurgle ['gə:gl] *gurgeln*
crawl [krɔ:l] *kriechen*
cover ['kʌvə] *(Bett)Decke*
spider ['spaidə] *Spinne*
shudder ['ʃʌdə] *schaudern, zittern*
fell quiet ['kwaiit] *von* fall quiet [fɔ:l] *ruhig liegen bleiben*
whine [wain] *winseln, wimmern*
soft [sɔft] *hier: leise*
puppy ['pʌpi] *junger Hund*
boot heel [bu:t hi:l] *Stiefelabsatz*
taste [teist] *Geschmack*
heave [hi:v] *sich heben und senken*

He walked °tiredly through the corral and into the pasture. His saddled horse came at his whistle. Automatically he °tightened the cinch, mounted and rode away, down the road to the valley. The °squat black shadow °traveled under him. The moon sailed high and white. The uneasy dogs °barked °monotonously.

At daybreak a °buckboard and pair trotted up to the ranch yard, °scattering the °chickens. A °deputy sheriff and a °coroner sat in the seat. Jim Moore half °reclined against his saddle in the °wagon-°box. His tired gelding followed behind. The deputy sheriff °set the brake and °wrapped the °lines around it. The men dismounted.

Jim asked, "Do I have to go in? I'm too tired and °wrought up to see it now."

The coroner °pulled his lip and °studied. "Oh, I °guess not. We'll °tend to things and look around."

Jim °sauntered away towards the water-trough. °"Say," he called, °"kind of clean up a little, will you? You know."

The men went on into the house.

In a few minutes they °emerged, carrying the °stiffened body between them. It was wrapped up in a °comforter. They °eased it up into the wagon-box. Jim walked back towards them. "Do I have to go in with you now?"

"Where's your wife, Mr. Moore?" the deputy sheriff °demanded.

"I don't know," he said °wearily. "She's °somewhere around."

lean [li:n] *sich lehnen* od. *beugen*
vomit ['vɔmit] *sich übergeben* od. *erbrechen*
straighten up ['streitn] *sich aufrichten*
dizzy ['dizi] *schwind(e)lig*

---

tired ['taied] *müde*
tighten ['taitn] *festziehen, -schnallen*
squat [skwɔt] *flach, platt(gedrückt)*
travel ['trævl], traveled AE = travelled BE *hier: wandern, laufen*
bark [bɑːk] *bellen*
monotonous [mə'nɔtnəs] *eintönig*
buckboard and pair [pɛə] *zweispänniger (leichter) Wagen*
scatter ['skætə] *zerstreuen, auseinanderjagen*
chicken ['tʃikin] *Huhn*
deputy sheriff ['depjuti 'ʃerif] *stellvertretender Sheriff*
coroner ['kɔrənə] *Untersuchungsrichter (in Fällen gewaltsamen od. plötzlichen Todes)*
reclined [ri'klaind] *zurückgelehnt*
wagon AE = waggon BE ['wægən] *vierrädriger Wagen*
box [bɔks] *(Wagen)Kasten*
set the brake [breik] *die Bremse anziehen*
wrap [ræp] *wickeln*
line [lain] *Leine*
wrought up [rɔːt] = worked up *aufgeregt*
pull one's lip *an der Lippe zupfen*
study ['stʌdi] *prüfend ansehen*
guess AE [ges] *glauben, denken*
tend to things *sich darum kümmern*
saunter ['sɔːntə] *schlendern*
say [sei] *hören Sie mal*
kind of clean up a little, will you? [kliːn] *Sie räumen doch auch ein bißchen auf, was?*
emerge [i'məːdʒ] *herauskommen*

"You're °sure you didn't °kill her too?"

"No. I didn't °touch her. I'll find her and bring her in this afternoon. °That is, if you don't want me to go in with you now."

"We've got your °statement," the coroner said. "And by God, we've got eyes, haven't we, Will? Of course there's a °technical charge of murder against you, but it'll be °dismissed. Always is in this part of the country. °Go kind of light on your wife, Mr. Moore."

"I won't °hurt her," said Jim.

He stood and watched the buckboard °jolt away. He °kicked his feet °reluctantly in the °dust. The hot June sun showed its face over the hills and °flashed °viciously on the bedroom window.

Jim went slowly into the house, and brought out a °nine-foot, °loaded °bull whip. He crossed the yard and walked into the barn. And as he °climbed the °ladder to the °hayloft, he heard the high, puppy whimpering start.

When Jim came out of the barn again, he carried Jelka over his shoulder. By the water-trough he set her °tenderly on the ground. Her hair was °littered with bits of hay. The back of her °shirtwaist was °streaked with blood.

Jim wetted his °bandana at the °pipe and washed her °bitten lips, and washed her face and °brushed back her hair. Her °dusty black eyes followed every °move he made.

"You hurt me," she said. "You hurt me °bad."

stiffened ['stifnd] *erstarrt, steif geworden*
comforter AE ['kʌmfətə] *Steppdecke*
ease [iːz] *vorsichtig* (hin)*legen*
demand [diˈmɑːnd] *fragen*
weary ['wiəri] *müde, matt, erschöpft*
somewhere around ['sʌmwɛə] (hier) *irgendwo*

---

sure [ʃuə] *sicher*
kill *töten*
touch [tʌtʃ] *an-, berühren*
that is *das heißt*
statement ['steitmənt] *Aussage*
technical charge of murder ['teknikəl tʃɑːdʒ] *formale Mordanklage*
dismiss [disˈmis] *abweisen, fallen lassen*
go kind of light on ... *gehen Sie einigermaßen glimpflich um mit ...*
hurt [həːt] *verletzen, weh tun*
jolt [dʒəult] *holpern*
kick (mit dem Fuß) *treten od. stoßen*
reluctant [riˈlʌktənt] *zögernd*
dust [dʌst] *Staub*
flash [flæʃ] (auf)*blitzen*
vicious ['viʃəs] *bösartig*
nine-foot ['nainˈfut] *neun Fuß lang* (1 foot = 30,48 cm)
loaded ['ləudid] *mit Blei beschwert*
bull whip [bul wip] *Rindlederpeitsche*
climb [klaim] (er)*steigen, steigen* (auf)
ladder ['lædə] *Leiter*
hayloft ['heiləft] *Heuboden*
tender ['tendə] *sanft, zart*
littered ['litəd] *übersät*
shirtwaist AE ['ʃəːtweist] *Hemdbluse*
streaked with blood [striːkt] *voll blutiger Streifen*
bandana [bænˈdænə] *großes buntes Taschen- od. Halstuch*
pipe [paip] (Brunnen)*Röhre*
bitten ['bitn] *zerbissen*
brush [brʌʃ] *hier: streichen*
dusty ['dʌsti] *hier: matt*
move [muːv] *Bewegung*
bad [bæd] = badly *hier: sehr*

He °nodded °gravely. °"Bad as I could without killing you."

The sun shone hotly on the ground. A few °blowflies °buzzed about, looking for the blood.

Jelka's °thickened lips tried to smile. "Did you have any breakfast °at all?"

"No," he said. °"None at all."

"Well, then, I'll °fry you up some eggs." She °struggled painfully to her feet.

"Let me help you," he said. "I'll help you °get your shirtwaist off. It's °drying stuck to your back. It'll hurt."

"No. I'll do it myself." Her voice had a °peculiar °resonance in it. Her dark eyes °dwelt warmly on him for a moment, and then she turned and °limped into the house.

Jim waited, sitting on the edge of the water-trough. He saw the smoke °start out of the °chimney and °sail °straight up into the air. In a very few moments Jelka called him from the kitchen door.

"Come, Jim. Your breakfast."

Four °fried eggs and four thick °slices of °bacon lay on a warmed °plate for him. "The coffee will be ready in a minute," she said.

°"Won't you eat?"

"No. Not now. °My mouth's too sore."

He ate his eggs hungrily and then looked up at her. Her black hair was °combed smooth. She had on a fresh white shirtwaist. "We're going to town this afternoon," he said. "I'm going to °order °lumber. We'll build a new house °farther down the canyon."

nod [nɔd] *nicken*
grave [greiv] *ernst*
bad as I could *so sehr ich konnte*

blowfly ['bləuflai] *Schmeißfliege*
buzz [bʌz] *summen*

thickened ['θikənd] *geschwollen*

at all [ə'tɔːl] *überhaupt*

none [nʌn] *kein(er, e, es)*

fry [frai] *braten*

struggle to one's feet ['strʌgl] *mühsam aufstehen*

get off *ausziehen, ablegen*

dry stuck to [drai, stʌk] *ankleben an*

peculiar [pi'kjuːljə] *eigenartig*
resonance ['rezənəns] *Mitschwingen*
dwelt [dwelt] *von* dwell [dwel] *hier: ruhen*
limp [limp] *hinken, humpeln*

start out of [staːt] *herauskommen, aufsteigen aus*
chimney ['tʃimni] *Schornstein*
sail [seil] *schweben, aufsteigen*
straight up [streit] *gerade od. senkrecht nach oben*

fried egg [fraid] *Spiegelei*

slice [slais] *Scheibe*
bacon ['beikən] *Speck*
plate [pleit] *Teller*

won't you [wəunt] = will you not
my mouth's sore ['mauθiz sɔː] *mir tut der Mund weh*

comb [kəum] *kämmen*

order ['ɔːdə] *bestellen*
lumber AE ['lʌmbə] *Bauholz*
farther ['faːðə] *weiter*

Her eyes °darted to the closed bedroom door and then back to him. "Yes," she said. "That will be good." And then, after a moment, "Will you °whip me any more—for this?"

"No, not any more, for this."

Her eyes smiled. She sat down on a chair beside him, and Jim put out his hand and stroked her hair and the back of her neck.

dart [dɑːt] *sich schnell bewegen, schießen*

whip [wip] *auspeitschen*

# The °Vigilante

°The great surge of emotion, the °milling and shouting of the people °fell °gradually to silence in the town park. A crowd of people still stood under the °elm trees, °vaguely lighted by a blue °street light °two °blocks away. A tired °quiet °settled on the people; some members of the °mob began to °sneak away into the darkness. The park lawn was °cut to pieces by the feet of the crowd.

Mike knew it was all over. He could feel the °let-down in himself. He was as °heavily weary as though he °had gone without sleep for °several nights, but it was a °dreamlike °weariness, a grey °comfortable weariness. He pulled his cap down over his eyes and °moved away, but before leaving the park he turned for one last look.

In the center of the mob someone had °lighted a °twisted newspaper and was holding it up. Mike could see how the flame °curled about the feet of the grey °naked body hanging from the elm tree. It seemed °curious to him that negroes °turn a °bluish grey when they are dead. The burning newspaper lighted the heads of the up-looking men, silent men and °fixed; °they didn't move their eyes from the °hanged man.

Mike felt a little °irritation at whoever it was who was trying to burn the body. He °turned to a man who stood

vigilante AE [vidʒi'lænti] *An-gehöriger e-r Bürgerwehr*
the great surge of emotion fell gradually to silence [greit sɜːdʒ, i'məuʃən, fel, 'grædʒu-əli, 'sailəns] *hier: die Wogen der Erregung glätteten sich allmählich*
milling ['miliŋ] *hier: Schieben*
fell to silence *von* fall to silence [fɔːl] *hier: verstummen*
gradually *langsam, allmählich*
elm (tree) [elm (triː)] *Ulme*
vague [veig] *hier: schwach*
street light AE [striːt lait] *Straßenlaterne*
block AE [blɔk] *Häuserreihe*
two blocks away AE *zwei Straßen entfernt*
quiet ['kwaiət] *Stille, Ruhe*
settle on ['setl] *hier: sich senken über*
mob [mɔb] *Mob, Pöbel*
sneak away [sniːk] *sich davonschleichen*
cut to pieces [kʌt, 'piːsiz] *zerstückeln, hier: zertrampeln*
let-down ['letdaun] *Nachlassen (der Erregung)*
heavily weary ['hevili 'wiəri] *benommen vor Müdigkeit*
had gone without [gɔn] *von* go without [gəu] *auskommen ohne, hier: nicht haben*
several ['sevrəl] *mehrere*
dreamlike ['driːmlaik] *traumhaft*
weariness ['wiərinis] *Müdigkeit*
comfortable ['kʌmfətəbl] *wohltuend, angenehm*
move away [muːv] *weggehen*
light [lait] *anzünden*
twisted ['twistid] *zusammengedreht*
curl [kɜːl] *hier: züngeln*
naked ['neikid] *nackt*
curious ['kjuəriəs] *seltsam*
turn [tɜːn] *werden*

beside him in the °near-darkness. °"That don't do no good," he said.

The man moved away without replying.

The newspaper °torch went out, leaving the park almost black by °contrast. But °immediately another twisted paper was lighted and held up against the feet. Mike °moved to another watching man. "That don't do no good," he °repeated. "He's dead now. They can't hurt him °none."

The second man °grunted but did not look away from the flaming paper. °"It's a good job," he said. °"This'll °save the °county a lot of money and no °sneaky °lawyers °getting in."

"That's what I say," Mike agreed. "No sneaky lawyers. But it don't do no good to try to burn him."

The man continued staring toward the flame. "Well, it °can't °do much harm, either."

Mike °filled his eyes with the scene. He felt that he was °dull. He wasn't seeing enough of it. Here was a thing he would want to remember later so he could tell about it, but the dull °tiredness seemed to °cut the °sharpness of the picture. His °brain told him this was a terrible and °important °affair, but his eyes and his feelings didn't agree. It was just °ordinary. Half an hour before, when he had been °howling with the mob and °fighting for a °chance to °help pull on the rope, then his °chest had been so full that he had found he was crying. But now everything was dead, everything °unreal;

bluish ['bluːiʃ] *bläulich*
fixed [fikst] *fest, unverwandt*
they didn't move their eyes from ['didnt, ðɛə, aiz] *sie ließen kein Auge von*
hanged man [hæŋd mæn] (*Auf-*) *Gehängte*
irritation at [iriˈteiʃən] *Ärger über*
turn to *sich wenden an*

near-darkness ['niəˈdɑːknis] *hier: Halbdunkel*
that don't do no good *sl.* [dɑunt, gud] (*doppelte Verneinung:*) *das ist doch sinnlos*
torch [tɔːtʃ] *Fackel*
contrast ['kɔntrɑːst] *Kontrast, Gegensatz*
immediately [iˈmiːdjətli] *sofort*
move to *gehen zu*
repeat [riˈpiːt] *wiederholen*
none *sl.* [nʌn] (*doppelte Verneinung:*) *in keiner Weise*
grunt [grʌnt] *brummen*
it's a good job [dʒɔb] *hier: gut gemacht!, so ist's recht!*
this'll ['ðisl] = this will
save [seiv] *ersparen*
county AE ['kaunti] (*Verwaltungs*)*Bezirk, Kreis*
sneaky ['sniːki] = sneaking *hinterlistig, gemein*
lawyer ['lɔːjə] (*Rechts*)*Anwalt*
get in *hier: sich einmischen*
can't ... either [kɑːnt, 'aiðə, AE 'iːðə] *kann auch nicht ...*
do harm [hɑːm] *schaden*
fill one's eyes with s.th. [wʌnz] *hier: s-e Augen registrieren et.*
dull [dʌl] *dumpf, träge*
tiredness ['taiədnis] *Müdigkeit*
cut *auflösen, hier: trüben*
sharpness ['ʃɑːpnis] *Schärfe*
brain [brein] *Verstand*
important [imˈpɔːtənt] *wichtig*
affair [əˈfɛə] *Angelegenheit*
ordinary ['ɔːdnri] *gewöhnlich*
howl [haul] *schreien, brüllen*
fight for [fait] *kämpfen um*
chance [tʃɑːns] *Gelegenheit*
help pull = help to pull
chest [tʃest] *Brust*

unreal ['ʌnˈriəl] *unwirklich*

the dark mob was °made up of °stiff °lay-figures. In the flamelight the faces were as °expressionless as wood. Mike felt the °stiffness, the °unreality in himself, too. He °turned away at last and walked out of the park.

The moment he left the °outskirts of the mob a cold loneliness °fell upon him. He walked quickly along the street wishing that some other man might be walking beside him. The wide street was °deserted, empty, as unreal as the park had been. The two °steel °lines of the °car °tracks °stretched °glimmering away down the street under the °electroliers, and the dark °store windows °reflected the midnight °globes.

A °gentle pain began to °make itself felt in Mike's chest. He felt with his fingers; the muscles were °sore. Then he remembered. He was in the front line of the mob when it °rushed the closed jail door. A °driving line °forty men deep had °crashed Mike against the door like the head of a °ram. He had hardly felt it then, and even now the pain seemed to have the dull °quality of loneliness.

°Two blocks ahead the burning neon word BEER hung over the °sidewalk. Mike hurried toward it. He hoped there would be people there, and talk, to °remove this silence; and he hoped the men wouldn't have been to the °lynching.

The °bartender was alone in his little bar, a small, °middle-aged man with a melancholy °moustache and an expression like an aged mouse, °wise and °unkempt and °fearful.

be made up of [meid] *sich zusammensetzen aus*
stiff *starr, steif*
lay-figure ['leiˈfigə] *Marionette*
expressionless [iksˈpreʃənlis] *ausdruckslos*
stiffness ['stifnis] *Starrheit*
unreality [ˈʌnriˈæliti] *Unwirklichkeit*
turn away *sich abwenden*
outskirts *Pl* ['autskə:ts] *hier: unmittelbare Umgebung*
fell upon *von* fall upon *herfallen über, hier: erfassen*
deserted [diˈzə:tid] *verlassen*
steel [sti:l] *stählern, Stahl...*
line [lain] *Linie; Gleis, Schiene*
car [kɑ:] *Straßenbahn(wagen)*
track [træk] *Gleis*
stretch away [stretʃ] *sich erstrecken*
glimmering ['gliməriŋ] *schimmernd*
electrolier [ilektrəuˈliə] *hier: elektrische Beleuchtung*
store [stɔ:] *Geschäft*
reflect [riˈflekt] *reflektieren, (wider)spiegeln*
globe [gləub] *Lampenglocke*
gentle ['dʒentl] *leicht*
make itself felt [meik, itself] *spürbar werden*
be sore [sɔ:] *weh tun*
rush [rʌʃ] *stürmen*
driving line ['draiviŋ] *vorwärtsdrängender Trupp*
forty men deep ['fɔ:ti men di:p] *vierzig Mann stark*
crash [kræʃ] *schmettern*
ram [ræm] *Rammbock, Ramme*
quality ['kwɔliti] *Beschaffenheit, Eigenart, Natur*
two blocks ahead AE [əˈhed] *zwei Straßen weiter vorn*
sidewalk AE ['saidwɔ:k] *Bürgersteig*
remove [riˈmu:v] *beseitigen*
lynching ['lintʃiŋ] *Lynchen*
bartender ['bɑ:tendə] *Barmixer*
middle-aged ['midlˈeidʒd] *mittleren Alters*
moustache [məsˈtɑ:ʃ] *Schnurrbart*
wise [waiz] *schlau, gerissen*
unkempt [ˈʌnˈkempt] *zerzaust*
fearful ['fiəful] *furchtsam*

He °nodded quickly as Mike came in. "You look °like you been °walking in your sleep," he said.

Mike °regarded him with °wonder. "That's just how I feel, too, °like I been walking in my sleep."

"Well, I can give you a °shot if you want."

Mike °hesitated. "No—I'm °kind of °thirsty. I'll take a beer. . . . °Was you there?"

The little man nodded his mouse-like head again. °"Right at the last, after he was all up and it was all over. I °figured a lot of the °fellas would be thirsty, so I came back and °opened up. Nobody but you so far. Maybe I was wrong."

°"They might be along later," said Mike. "There's a lot of them still in the park. They °cooled off, °though. °Some of them trying to burn him with newspapers. That don't do no good."

°"Not a bit of good," said the little bartender. He °twitched his thin moustache.

Mike knocked a few °grains of °celery salt into his beer and °took a long drink. "That's good," he said. "I'm kind of °dragged out."

The bartender leaned °close to him over the bar, his eyes were °bright. "Was you there all the time—to the jail and everything?"

Mike drank again and then looked through his beer and watched the °beads of °bubbles °rising from the grains

nod [nɔd] (mit dem Kopf) nicken
like you (I) been sl. [laik, biːn] = as if you (I) have been
walk in one's sleep [wɔːk, sliːp] nachtwandeln
regard [riˈgɑːd] betrachten
wonder [ˈwʌndə] Verwunderung, Staunen
shot F [ʃɔt] Gläschen (Schnaps etc.)
hesitate [ˈheziteit] zögern
kind of F [kaind] etwas, irgendwie
thirsty [ˈθəːsti] durstig
was you there sl. = were you there
right at the last [rait, lɑːst] erst ganz zum Schluß
figure AE F [ˈfigə] meinen, glauben
fella AE F [ˈfelə] = fellow [ˈfeləu] Bursche, Kerl
open up [ˈəupən] öffnen

they might be along later F [mait, əˈlɔŋ, ˈleitə] sie können ja noch kommen
cool off [kuːl] sich beruhigen
though F [ðəu] aber, allerdings
some of them trying sl. [sʌm, ˈtraiiŋ] = some of them were trying

not a bit keine Spur, nicht im geringsten
twitch [twitʃ] zupfen an

grain [grein] Korn, Körnchen
celery [ˈseləri] Sellerie
took a long drink [tuk, lɔŋ driŋk] von take a long drink [teik] hier: e-n kräftigen Schluck nehmen
dragged out sl. [drægd] erledigt, erschöpft
close [kləus] nah, dicht
bright [brait] glänzend

bead [biːd] Perle
bubble [ˈbʌbl] Blase
rise [raiz] aufsteigen

of salt in the °bottom of the glass. "Everything," he said. "I was one of the first in the jail, and I helped pull on the rope. °There's times when °citizens °got to take the °law in their own hands. Sneaky lawyer comes along and gets some °fiend out of it."

The °mousy head °jerked up and down. ""You °Goddam' right," he said. "Lawyers can get them out of anything. I °guess the °nigger was °guilty °all right."

"Oh, °sure! Somebody said he even °confessed."

The head came close over the bar again. "How did it start, °mister? I was only there after it was all over, and then I only stayed a minute and then came back to open up °in case any of the fellas might want a glass of beer."

Mike °drained his glass and °pushed it out to be filled. "Well, of course everybody knew it was going to happen. I was in a bar °across from the jail. °Been there all afternoon. A °guy came in and °says, 'What are we °waiting for?' So we went °across the street, and a lot more guys °was there and a lot more °come. We all stood there and °yelled. Then the °sheriff °come out and °made a speech, but we yelled him down. A guy with a °twenty-two rifle went along the street and shot out the street lights. Well, then we rushed the jail doors and °bust them. The sheriff wasn't going to do °nothing. It wouldn't do him °no good to °shoot a lot of °honest men to °save a nigger fiend."

bottom ['bɔtəm] *Boden*

there's times *sl.* [taimz] = there are times
citizen ['sitizn] *Bürger(in)*
got F [gɔt] = must
law [lɔː] *Gesetz, Recht*
fiend [fiːnd] *Teufel, hier: Verbrecher, übler Kerl*
mousy ['mausi] *mauseartig, Mäuse...*
jerk up and down [dʒəːk] *sich auf u. ab bewegen*
you right *sl.* = you are right
Goddam' = Goddamned *sl.* ['gɔdæm(d)] *verdammt*
guess AE [ges] *glauben, denken, annehmen*
nigger F ['nigə] *Nigger (verächtlich für Neger, Schwarze)*
guilty ['gilti] *schuldig*
all right *hier: doch wohl*
sure AE F [ʃuə] *aber sicher!, klar!*
confess [kən'fes] *gestehen*
mister ['mistə] *Herr!, Chef!*
in case [keis] *falls*

drain [drein] *bis zur Neige austrinken od. leeren*
push out [puʃ] *vorschieben*
across [ə'krɔs] *gegenüber; über*
been *sl.* = I had been
guy AE *sl.* [gai] *Bursche, Kerl*
says *sl.* [sez] = said [sed]
wait for [weit] *warten auf*
was there *sl.* = were there
come *sl.* [kʌm] = came [keim]
yel [jel] *schreien, brüllen*
sheriff ['ʃerif] *Sheriff*
come out *sl.* = came out
made a speech [spiːtʃ] *von make a speech [meik] e-e Rede halten*
twenty-two rifle ['raifl] *22er-Gewehr*
bust *sl.* [bʌst] *hier: aufsprengen*
nothing *sl.* ['nʌθiŋ] = anything ['eniθiŋ]
no good *sl.* = any good
shoot [ʃuːt] *erschießen*
honest ['ɔnist] *rechtschaffen, ehrlich*
save *retten*

"And °election °coming on, too," the bartender °put in.

"Well, the sheriff started yelling, 'Get the right man, boys, °for Christ's sake get the right man. He's in the fourth °cell down.'

"It was kind of °pitiful," Mike said slowly. "The other prisoners °was so scared. We could see them through the °bars. I never °seen such faces."

The bartender °excitedly °poured himself a small glass of °whiskey and °poured it down. °"Can't blame 'em much. °Suppose °you was in for thirty days and a °lynch mob came through. °You'd be scared °they'd get the wrong man."

"That's what I say. It was kind of pitiful. Well, we got to the nigger's cell. He just stood stiff with his eyes closed °like he was °dead drunk. One of the guys °slugged him down and he got up, and then somebody else °socked him and he °went over and °hit his head on the °cement floor." Mike leaned over the bar and °tapped the polished wood with his °forefinger. °" 'Course this is only my idea, but I think that killed him. Because I °helped get his clothes off, and he never made a °wiggle, and when we °strung him up °he didn't °jerk around none. No, sir. I think he was dead all the time, after that second guy °smacked him."

"Well, °it's all the same in the end."

"No, it °ain't. You like to do the thing right. °He had it coming to him, and he should have got it." Mike °reached into his trousers pocket and

election [i'lekʃən] *Wahl*
come on *hier: bevorstehen*
put in *einwerfen (Bemerkung)*

for Christ's sake [kraists seik] *um Christi od. Himmels willen*
cell [sel] *(Gefängnis)Zelle*

pitiful ['pitiful] *mitleiderregend*

was so scared *sl.* [skɛəd] = were so scared *hatten solche Angst*
bars *Pl* [bɑːz] *Gitter(stäbe)*
seen *sl.* = have seen
excited [ik'saitid] *aufgeregt, erregt*
pour o.s. s.th. [pɔː] *sich et. eingießen od. -schenken*
whiskey AE ['wiski] *Whisky*
pour down *hier: F kippen*
can't blame 'em (= them) much [kɑːnt, bleim, (ð)əm, mʌtʃ] *das kann ich ihnen nicht verdenken*
suppose [sə'pəuz] *annehmen, sich vorstellen*
you was *sl.* = you were
lynch mob [lintʃ] *Lynchmob*
you'd = you would
they'd = (that) they would
like he was *sl.* = as if he were
dead drunk [ded drʌŋk] *total betrunken*
slug down [slʌg] *niederschlagen*
sock *sl.* [sɔk] *schlagen*
went over *von* go over *hier: umfallen*
hit *hier: aufschlagen mit*
cement [si'ment] *Zement*
tap [tæp] *klopfen auf*
forefinger ['fɔːfiŋgə] *Zeigefinger*
'course F [kɔːs] = of course
helped get = helped to get
wiggle ['wigl] *(windende) Bewegung*
strung s.o. up F [strʌŋ] *von* string s.o. up [striŋ] *j-n aufknüpfen*
he didn't . . . none *sl. (doppelte Verneinung) hier: überhaupt nicht*
jerk around *hier: herumzappeln*
smack [smæk] *schlagen*

°brought out a piece of °torn blue °denim. "That's a piece of the °pants he °had on."

The bartender bent close and °inspected the °cloth. He °jerked his head up at Mike. "I'll give you a °buck for it."

"Oh no, you won't!"

"All right. I'll give you two bucks for half of it."

Mike looked °suspiciously at him. °"What you want it for?"

"Here! Give me your glass! °Have a beer on me. I'll °pin it up on the wall with a little card under it. The fellas that come in will like to look at it."

Mike °haggled the piece of cloth in two with his pocket knife and °accepted two silver dollars from the bartender.

"I know a °show card writer," the little man said. "Comes in every day. He'll °print me up a nice little card to °go under it." He looked °wary. °"Think the sheriff will °arrest anybody?"

" 'Course not. °What's he want to start any trouble for? There was a lot of °votes in that crowd tonight. °Soon as they all go away, the sheriff will come and cut the nigger down and °clean up °some."

The bartender looked toward the door. "I guess I was wrong about the fellas wanting a drink. It's °getting late."

"I guess I'll get along home. I feel tired."

"If you go south, I'll close up and walk °a ways with you. I °live on south Eighth."

"Why, that's only two blocks from my house. I live on south Sixth. You must go right °past my house. Funny I never saw you around."

The bartender washed Mike's glass and °took off the long °apron. He °put on his hat and coat, walked to the door and °switched off the red neon °sign and the house lights. For a moment the two men stood on the sidewalk looking back toward the park. The city was silent. There was no sound from the park. A policeman walked along a block away, turning his °flash into the store windows.

°"You see?" said Mike. °"Just like nothing happened."

"Well, if the fellas wanted a glass of beer they must have gone °someplace else."

"That's what I told you," said Mike.

They °swung along the empty street and °turned south, out of the °business district. "My name's Welch," the bartender said. "I only °been in this town about two years."

The loneliness had fallen on Mike again. "It's funny—" he said, and then, "I was born right in this town, right in the house I °live in now. I °got a wife but no °kids. Both of us °born right in this town. Everybody knows us."

They walked on for a few blocks. The stores °dropped behind and the nice houses with °bushy gardens and °cut lawns °lined the street. The tall °shade

---

a ways [weiz] *ein Stück*
live on [liv] *wohnen in (Straße)*

past [pɑːst] *an ... vorbei*

took off [tuk] *von* take off *abnehmen, ausziehen*
apron ['eiprən] *Schürze*
put on *aufsetzen (Hut); anziehen (Mantel)*
switch off [switʃ] *ausschalten*
sign [sain] *Schild*

flash AE [flæʃ] = flashlight *Taschenlampe*

you see? F *verstehen Sie?, hier: sehen Sie?*
just like = just as if

someplace AE ['sʌmpleis] *irgendwo(hin)*

swung [swʌŋ] *von* swing [swiŋ] *flott gehen od. marschieren*
turn *abbiegen od. sich wenden nach*
business district ['biznis 'distrikt] *Geschäftsviertel*
been *sl.* = have been

live in *wohnen in (Haus)*
got AE F = have
kid [kid] *Kind*
born *sl.* [bɔːn] = were born
drop behind [drɔp bi'haind] *zurückbleiben*
bushy ['buʃi] *voller Büsche, mit Büschen bewachsen*
cut *(zu)geschnitten, hier: gepflegt*
line [lain] *säumen*
shade tree [ʃeid] *schattenspendender Baum, Schattenbaum*

91

trees °were shadowed on the sidewalk by the street lights. Two night dogs °went slowly by, °smelling at each other.

Welch said softly—°"I wonder °what kind of a fella he was—the nigger, I mean."

Mike answered out of his loneliness. "The °papers all said he was a fiend. I read all the papers. That's what they all said."

"Yes, I read them, too. But °it makes you wonder about him. I've known some °pretty nice niggers."

Mike turned his head and spoke °protestingly. "Well, °I've knew some °dam' °fine niggers myself. I've worked right °'longside some niggers and °they was as nice as any white man you could want to meet.—But °not no fiends."

His °vehemence °silenced little Welch for a moment. Then he said, "You couldn't tell, I guess, what kind of a fella he was?"

"No—he just stood there stiff, with his mouth shut and his eyes °tight closed and his hands right down at his sides. And then one of the guys smacked him. It's my idea he was dead when we took him out."

Welch °sidled close °on the walk. "Nice gardens along here. Must take a lot of money to °keep them up." He walked even closer, so that his shoulder touched Mike's arm. "I never °been to a lynching. °How's it make you feel— °afterwards?"

Mike °shied away from the °contact. °"'It don't make you feel nothing." He put down his head and °increased

were shadowed ... by the street lights ['ʃædəud] *hier: die Straßenlaternen warfen die dunklen Umrisse ...*
went by *von* go by *vorbei-, vorübergehen*
smelling at each other ['smelɪŋ, iːtʃ, 'ʌðə] *hier: sich beschnuppernd*
I wonder ['wʌndə] *ich frage mich, ich möchte gern wissen*
what kind of a ... *was für ein...*
paper ['peipə] = *newspaper*
it makes you wonder *man möchte doch et. mehr wissen*

pretty ['priti] *ziemlich, ganz*

protesting [prə'testiŋ] *protestierend*
I've knew *sl.* [njuː] = I have known [nəun]
dam' = damned *sl.* [dæm(d)] *verdammt, -flucht*
fine [fain] *ausgezeichnet, hier: anständig, nett*
'longside F = alongside [(ə)'lɔŋ'said] *neben, Seite an Seite*
they was *sl.* = they were
not no *sl. (doppelte Verneinung im Dialekt)*
vehemence ['viːiməns] *Heftigkeit*
silence ['sailəns] *zum Schweigen bringen*
tight [tait] *fest*
sidle close ['saidl kləus] *dicht herankommen*
on the walk [wɔːk] *beim Gehen*
keep up [kiːp] *hier: instand halten*
been *sl.* = have been
how's *sl.* = how does
afterwards ['ɑːftəwədz] *hinterher, später*
shied away [ʃaid] *von* shy away [ʃai] *zurückschrecken*
contact ['kɔntækt] *Berührung*
it don't make you feel nothing *sl.* = it doesn't make you feel anything
increase [in'kriːs] *steigern, erhöhen, hier: beschleunigen*

his °pace. The little bartender had °nearly to °trot °to keep up. The street lights were fewer. It was darker and safer. Mike °burst out, "Makes you feel kind of °cut off and tired, but kind of °satisfied, too. °Like you done a good job—but tired and kind of sleepy." He °slowed his °steps. "Look, there's a light in the kitchen. That's where I live. My °old lady's °waiting up for me." He stopped in front of his little house.

Welch stood nervously beside him. "Come into my place when you want a glass of beer—or a shot. Open till midnight. I °treat my friends right." He °scampered away like an aged mouse.

Mike called, "Good night."

He walked around the side of his house and went in the back door. His thin, °petulant wife was sitting by the open gas °oven warming herself. She °turned °complaining eyes on Mike where he stood in the °doorway.

Then her eyes widened and hung on his face. "You °been with a woman," she said °hoarsely. "What woman you been with?"

Mike laughed. "You think you're pretty °slick, don't you? You're a slick one, °ain't you? What makes you think I °been with a woman?"

She said °fiercely, "You think I can't °tell by the °look on your face that you been with a woman?"

"All right," said Mike. "If you're so slick and °know-it-all, I °won't tell you nothing. You can just wait for the morning paper."

pace [peis] *Tempo*

nearly ['niəli] *fast, beinahe*
trot [trɔt] *Trab laufen*
to keep up *um Schritt halten zu können*
burst out [bəːst] *herausplatzen*
cut off *losgelöst, abgeschnitten, einsam*
satisfied ['sætisfaid] *befriedigt, zufrieden*
like you done *sl.* [dʌn] = *as if you had done*
slow [sləu] *verlangsamen*
step *Schritt*
old lady F [əuld 'leidi] *Alte (Ehefrau)*
wait up for s.o. *aufbleiben u. auf j-n warten*

treat s.o. right [triːt] *j-n gut bewirten od. bedienen*
scamper away ['skæmpə] *sich davonmachen*

petulant ['petjulənt] *verdrießlich, gereizt*
oven ['ʌvn] *Backofen*
turn on *richten auf*
complaining [kəm'pleiniŋ] *hier: anklagend*
doorway ['dɔːwei] *Türöffnung, (Tür)Eingang*
been *sl.* = *have been*
hoarse [hɔːs] *heiser*

slick F [slik] *schlau, raffiniert*
ain't you *sl.* = *aren't you*

fierce [fiəs] *wütend, heftig*
tell *erkennen*
look [luk] *(Gesichts)Ausdruck*

know-it-all ['nəuitɔːl] *besserwisserisch, klugscheißerisch*
won't tell you nothing *sl.* = *will not tell you anything*

He saw doubt come into the °dissatis-
fied eyes. "Was it the nigger?" she
asked. "Did they get the nigger? Everybody said °they was going to."

"Find out for yourself if you're so
slick. °I ain't going to tell you nothing."

He walked through the kitchen and
went into the bathroom. A little mirror
hung on the wall. Mike took off his
cap and looked at his face. "By God,
she was right," he thought. "That's just
°exactly how I do feel."

dissatisfied ['dis'sætisfaid] *verdrießlich, unzufrieden*

they was *sl.* = they were

I ain't ... nothing *sl.* = I am
not ... anything

exactly [ig'zæktli] *genau*

### Langenscheidts Großes Schulwörterbuch Englisch

Englisch-Deutsch
Von Heinz Messinger. 1440 Seiten.

Deutsch-Englisch
Von Heinz Messinger. 1328 Seiten.

Format jeweils 11,8 × 18,5 cm, gebunden.
Rund 200 000 Stichwörter in beiden Teilen.

Bei gleichem Inhalt wie das Handwörterbuch ist es besonders
lernpraktisch für die gymnasiale Oberstufe, für
Fremdsprachenkurse in der Erwachsenenbildung und im
Studium. Durch vergrößerte Schrift, optimale Lesbarkeit und das
kleinere Format.

### The Oxford English-Reader's Dictionary

Von A. S. Hornby und E. C. Parnwell.
638 Seiten. Format 11,8 × 18,5 cm. Gebunden.

Ein Wörterbuch mit englischen Definitionen, das auf die
besonderen Erfordernisse in den deutschsprachigen Ländern
abgestimmt ist. Mit 500 erläuternden Illustrationen zu den rund
40 000 Stichwörtern.

### Englisch diskutieren

Von Heinz-Otto Hohmann. 88 Seiten.
Format 12,4 × 19,2 cm, kartoniert-laminiert.

Englisch-deutscher Diskussionswortschatz mit Satzbeispielen.
Parallelanordnung Englisch-Deutsch. Mit deutschem Register.
Für Schule, Alltag und Beruf.

### 1000 englische Redensarten

Neubearbeitung von der Langenscheidt-Redaktion und
R. J. Quinault. 239 Seiten, illustriert. Format 12,4 × 19,2 cm,
kartoniert-laminiert.

Eine Zusammenstellung idiomatischer Redensarten, die zum
vollen Verständnis der englischen Sprache unentbehrlich sind.
Nach Stichwörtern alphabetisch geordnet. Mit deutschem
Register. Reichhaltig illustriert.

# Langenscheidt ... weil Sprachen verbinden

### Langenscheidts Grammatiktafel Englisch

16 Seiten kartoniert, Format 14,8 × 21 cm.

Grammatik auf einen Blick!
Sie enthält konzentriert alle wichtigen grammatischen
Erscheinungen des Englischen. Der Lernende spart sich
zeitraubendes Blättern, da er die Tafel vor sich aufstellen kann.
Farben erleichtern das Orientieren.

### Langenscheidts Englische Grammatik
### in Frage und Antwort

Format 10,5 × 18,2 × 3 cm, in Kartonschuber.

Eine Grammatikkartei, die sich hervorragend zum Wiederholen
und Festigen grammatischer Kenntnisse eignet. Sie enthält 200
Karten, mit denen die grammatischen Regeln im Selbstunterricht
wiederholt und aufgrund der Beispiele leicht eingeprägt werden
können.

### Langenscheidts Wortschatzkarteien Englisch

Englisch I – Die 1000 wichtigsten Wörter
Englisch II – Die wichtigsten Wörter – Das zweite Tausend.

Je 1000 Karten (4 × 10 cm) mit englischen Vokabeln
(Vorderseite) und Übersetzungen (Rückseite).
In Spezialkartons, Format 11 × 22,7 × 4,5 cm.

Diese Wortschatzkarteien basieren auf den neuesten
wissenschaftlichen Worthäufigkeitszählungen. Mit ihnen ist ein
systematisches Wörterlernen bzw. Wiederholen möglich.

### Teste Dein Englisch!

Von Geoffrey Broughton

Stufe 1: Testbuch für Anfänger (208 Seiten)
Stufe 2: Testbuch für Fortgeschrittene (222 Seiten)
Stufe 3: Testbuch für Könner (224 Seiten)

Format jeweils 11 × 18 cm, kartoniert-laminiert.

In einem anregenden, amüsanten Frage- und Antwortspiel lernt
der Benutzer, wie man die für den Ausländer typischen Fehler
vermeidet.

# Langenscheidt ... weil Sprachen verbinden